THE ECONOMICS OF
SUBSISTENCE AGRICULTURE

The Economics of

Subsistence Agriculture

BY

COLIN CLARK

M.A. (Oxon.), M.A. (Cantab.), Hon. D.Sc. (Milan)
Hon. D.Ec. (Tilburg)

Professorial Fellow of Brasenose College, Oxford
Director, Agricultural Economics Research Institute, Oxford

AND

MARGARET HASWELL

B.Litt., M.A. (Oxon.)

Demonstrator and Administrative Officer
Agricultural Economics Research Institute, Oxford

ST MARTIN'S PRESS

1964

Copyright © Colin Clark and Margaret Haswell 1964

MACMILLAN AND COMPANY LIMITED
St Martin's Street London WC 2
also Bombay Calcutta Madras Melbourne

THE MACMILLAN COMPANY OF CANADA LIMITED
Toronto

ST MARTIN'S PRESS INC
New York

PRINTED IN GREAT BRITAIN

Contents

List of Tables

List of Charts

Acknowledgments

The authors wish to acknowledge the help they have received from Mr. P. Martin in preparing material for this book, and from Mrs. R. M. C. Fasnacht and Mrs. M. Holland in preparing the manuscript for press. They also gratefully acknowledge permission to draw upon material by one of the authors previously appearing in Royal Statistical Society and Ciba Foundation publications.

CHAPTER I

Food Requirements

Alifetime of malnutrition and actual hunger is the lot of at least two-thirds of mankind.' This extraordinary mis-statement, which is in fact based on an arithmetical error, is believed by almost everyone, because they have heard it so often; people come to think that any statement which they have heard repeated frequently enough (as Hitler pointed out) must be true. This lack of critical sense however is particularly reprehensible in the prominent men of letters and scientists whose repetition of the statement has done so much to secure its acceptance, men accustomed in their own field to making the most careful and critical judgements, but apparently willing to accept any sort of statement without evidence as soon as they go outside them. Under these circumstances (as Hitler once again pointed out) it is both easier and more profitable to get people to believe a large falsehood than a small one.

Social psychologists may take this almost universal circulation of a statement demonstrably false as yet another example of the unbalanced state of mind of a generation prone to faction and extremism (now perhaps being replaced by a more rational younger generation?).

This statement was first made in 1950 by Lord Boyd Orr,[1] who had just retired from the post of Director-General of FAO (Food and Agriculture Organization of the United Nations). A search for the evidence on which this statement is supposed to have been based provides a most interesting intellectual detective story, and yields an astonishing result. This search was undertaken by M. K. Bennett,[2] Director of the Food Research Institute at Stanford University, and a recognized world authority in this field. In the years since 1954 no reply of any kind to Bennett has been made by Lord Boyd Orr, or by anyone speaking on his behalf.

Bennett carefully scrutinized the text of FAO's 'Second World Food Survey', which was not published until 1952, but which

[1] In *Scientific American*, New York, August 1950.
[2] In his book, *The World's Food*, Harper Brothers, New York, 1954.

appears to have contained the material on which Lord Boyd Orr was working. This survey included a statistical table, for which neither sources nor methods of compilation were given, purporting to show average calorie requirements per head of all the nations in the world, and comparing these with supposed data of calorie supplies — data which, for most of the countries in question, have not since been republished, because of serious doubts about their accuracy.

These very dubious calculations (which showed, for instance, that Portugal was seriously undernourished, but not Spain) nevertheless fixed figures for supposed calorie requirements well below FAO's earlier 'estimates'. But Bennett's examination of Lord Boyd Orr's text compels him to conclude — 'one cannot escape the inference' — that he had completely mixed up the statistics (inaccurate in any case) which had been placed before him; and had taken as supposed minimum requirements, below which people would actually suffer hunger, a set of figures of 'targets' for production at some time in the future (which targets FAO itself had in fact already abandoned).

The scientific measurement of man's food requirements is a task which was begun comparatively late in the history of physiology and biochemistry, and is yet far from complete. As in all branches of science, conclusions reached on the subject of human nutrition must be tentative, claiming only to summarize the best knowledge at present available. Many, however, have written on this subject with an extreme dogmatism, which will not stand up to scientific questioning.

Food — leaving aside questions of taste and enjoyment — has to serve a number of physiological purposes, the first and most immediate of which is to maintain bodily activity and warmth. This purpose is served in varying degree by all foods; the contribution to it of various foods can be measured precisely in terms of the single unit of energy, the calorie. (It used to be held that calories could not be regarded as entirely homogeneous as sources of our food energy, but that it was necessary for us to receive a certain proportion of them in the form of fat. This proposition is, however, very doubtful physiologically, although there may be a case for it on the grounds of taste and palatability.)

After the provision of energy, the next most important function of food, if we may use the analogy of the factory, is the performance of 'essential maintenance work'. All the muscles and organs of the body need repair, some almost continuously, others intermittently. The performance of these repairs is not primarily a function of the energy foods, but requires a large and highly differentiated group of chemical compounds, the proteins,[1] which depend upon the element nitrogen, organized into certain chemical structures. We pass tons of plain nitrogen through our lungs every year without being able to use any of it; it is only after some difficult chemical syntheses have been performed for us by plants or animals that we can get it into our diet.

As each muscle or organ of the body is repaired, the worn-out piece is broken up into what might be called 'scrap', large chemical molecules which go back into circulation in the bloodstream, from which they are used again to perform some of the simpler repairing tasks. So well organized is the biochemistry of the human body that each atom of nitrogen, it has been computed, can be used three or four times, in performing successively simpler tasks, until finally it has reached the chemical stage where it cannot be used further, and has to be excreted in the urine.

While not essential (beyond certain very small quantities), animal proteins are for certain purposes more efficacious than vegetable proteins. A person dependent upon vegetable protein may therefore have to consume more in the aggregate.

It has long been known that certain quantities of mineral elements, particularly iron and calcium, were required in the diet, though the precise amount is still debatable. Starting with Hopkins's discoveries in 1906, it has been found since that a great variety of 'accessory food factors' (now called vitamins) are necessary for health, though only required in small quantities. Later it was discovered that man, like plants and animals, requires very small quantities of a great variety of mineral 'trace elements'.

Research work now proceeding also indicates that, out of the great variety of edible fats, a certain limited number (belonging chemically to the 'unsaturated' group) are necessary for health, and that their absence may eventually lead to grave arterial disease; and at the same time it appears (though there is some division of medical opinion on this question) that certain other fats may do positive harm in this respect if consumed in too large quantities, particularly the fats found in the milk and the meat of ruminant animals.

[1] Named after the sea god Proteus, famous in Greek mythology for the bewildering variety of forms which he could assume. The chemist who discovered proteins was a classical scholar.

There is no doubt that shortages of vitamins and minerals in the diet may have serious effects upon health, and may sometimes be fatal. Though it cannot be said with complete finality, it seems however to be generally agreed among those who have studied this subject that such shortages (likewise shortages of unsaturated fats relative to other fats) are not very likely to arise in a primitive nomadic or peasant community whose food, scanty though it be, is nevertheless directly obtained from natural sources. Such peoples consume their cereals or meats in comparatively unprocessed form, and supplement them with a variety of other natural products, such as wild salad plants, seaweeds, snails, fungi and many others. Deficiencies of vitamins and minerals may occur through a more or less accidental event, as when the custom of polishing rice in certain Asian communities led to a spread of beri-beri, or among the poorer sections of industrial communities, living upon foods which, by the nature of things, have been selected for their transportability and storability, and which may have been transported, processed and stored in ways which may have caused them to lose some of their mineral and vitamin components.

Another feature of deficiencies of vitamins and minerals is that most of such deficiencies known so far can be easily and cheaply remedied by the mixing of very small quantities of chemical preparations in other foods. However, in view of the possible existence of other such food factors which may not yet have been discovered, it is advisable to continue to include a wide range of variegated natural foods in the diet.

The meat, dairy produce, fruit, etc., which predominate in our diets, while much more agreeable — none of us would like to live on a diet computed to meet physiological minimum requirements, consisting mainly of porridge — nevertheless should be regarded as amenities rather than physiological necessities.

For poor peasant communities therefore our first question should be on the availability of calories and proteins.

FAO was once sardonically described by *The Economist*[1] as 'a permanent institution devoted to proving that there is not enough food in the world'. There is unfortunately a considerable element of truth in this accusation; though it is also true, as *The Economist* went on to admit, that FAO has rendered great service to the world by giving 'much useful practical advice and assistance'

[1] 23 August 1952.

regarding food production and distribution throughout the world.

One of the most important tasks which FAO has undertaken has been to organize the preparation, by a group of the leading physiologists in this field, of thorough and agreed studies of what are in fact people's food requirements, measured in calories, under varying circumstances, the first published in 1950, and an improved and enlarged version in 1957.[1] This valuable scientific report provides the basis for the calculations given below.

FAO has now however acquired a sort of collective personality, and tends, like other organisms, to make self-preservation its first aim. The public relations department thus takes precedence over the Statistics Division. FAO first decides upon and announces a 'World Freedom from Hunger Campaign', and then proceeds to look for the statistical evidence on which to base it. The leading FAO spokesmen, while not feeling entirely bound by Lord Boyd Orr's statement, which he made after he had retired from the Director-Generalship, nevertheless thought that they wanted a figure not too different from his, and decided that it should be half the world which was suffering from malnutrition. Some of the statements designed to prove this, for example Sir Norman Wright's address to the British Association for the Advancement of Science in Cardiff in September 1960, fixed a very high level of minimum requirements, in complete disregard of the conclusions reached by FAO's own expert committee on calorie requirements.

In May 1961 FAO's own Director of Statistics, Dr. Sukhatme, an Indian, in a paper[2] to the Royal Statistical Society in London, making a mathematical analysis of the limited information available on the distribution of food consumption in Asia, concluded that the proportion of the world's population which was hungry was 10 to 15 per cent. Discussion by an expert audience confirmed this conclusion, subject to the possibility that the extent of hunger in China might be rather greater, and in the rest of Asia rather less, than Dr. Sukhatme had stated.

It has therefore become necessary for FAO spokesmen to explain this difference between this 10–15 per cent and their 50 per cent of the world's population, which is after all a very large number of people, as representing some form of 'malnutrition' in respect of

---

[1] FAO Nutritional Studies, *Calorie Requirements*; No. 5, 1950; No. 15, 1957.
[2] *Journal of the Royal Statistical Society*, Series A, Part 4, 1961.

nutrients which have not been specified, and for which not the smallest fragment of evidence has been produced.[1]

But is it not the case, many people may ask, that it is possible to have a diet adequate in calories, or 'starchy foods', but still to suffer serious malnutrition through lack of adequate quantities of the (emotively named) 'protective foods'? When one of the writers was working with Lord Boyd Orr in the 1930s, this was clearly understood. We required 100 g. of fat per head per day, 68 g. of protein, at least half of which must be obtained from animal sources, 0·9 g. of calcium, which must be obtained from dairy products and vegetables, not by enriching flour; and so on. Subsequent advances in physiological science, fortified by the experience of medical administrators during the war years, when they had real famines to deal with, in both Europe and Asia, have caused all these figures to be abandoned; though of course there is always a time lag between scientific and popular knowledge, and a great many people (and governments) are still acting on the out-of-date information. It was Sir Norman Wright who stated, immediately after the war, that while a certain amount of fat undoubtedly made the diet more palatable, there was no physiological need for any fat consumption at all. During subsequent years, as many physiologists and doctors have proclaimed that the consumption of large quantities of fat, particularly in dairy produce and in meat from ruminant animals, and artificially hardened vegetable fats, was positively harmful, the consumption of such fats has already fallen heavily, particularly in the U.S.A.

Regarding protein requirements, FAO attempted to follow up its report on calorie requirements with a similar study for protein. With the best of learning and goodwill, the leading experts in this field were quite unable to come to anything like an agreed conclusion on this extremely complex subject. Some recent work, however,[2] has indicated that true protein needs may not be much more than half of what was previously supposed. If the protein is of good quality, Brock would put adult protein needs at as low as

[1] Since the above was written, FAO's *Third World Food Survey* has become available. This document defends the original contention that half the world's population suffers from either hunger or malnutrition by some calculations based on the proposition that a person is malnourished unless he derives at least 20 per cent of his total calorie intake from animal products, fruits and vegetables, and fats and oils. No backing is given for this proposition, which indeed runs counter to all the available physiological evidence, apart from the statement that 'it is generally agreed'. (p. 9.)

[2] Professor Waterlow, Jamaica, and Professor Brock, Cape Town; private communications.

$\frac{1}{2}$ g./kg. body weight/day (with higher figures for children, rising to a maximum of 3). Other requirements he would also put much lower than previously supposed; calcium at 0·3 instead of 0·8 g./day, and Vitamin C at 25 instead of 75 mg./day. Waterlow puts requirements of *first-class* protein, all in g./kg. body weight/day, for an infant under 6 months at 1·5 (7 g./day in all), falling to 0·5 at puberty, and 0·35 for adults. For pregnancy he adds 0·4 and for lactation 0·2.

As for the supposed requirement that half the protein intake be in the form of protein from animal products (meat, fish, eggs and dairy products), it should have occurred to those who made this statement that there have been and are very large numbers of people in Europe as well as in Asia who, for religious or customary reasons, have been vegetarians throughout their lives, and who have consumed little or no dairy produce either. Several doctors[1] have been able to study some members of a European religious group, the Vegans, whose vegetarianism is so strict that they do not allow themselves to consume dairy products or eggs (or even honey), which are consumed by some vegetarians. Sinclair persuaded a number of members of this group to come to the Radcliffe Hospital in Oxford for a thorough physiological examination, and was unable to find any defects, except for a possibility of a qualification regarding supplies of Vitamin B_{12} which perhaps can be obtained only from animal sources. In treating patients (mainly children) known to be suffering from serious protein deficiency (called *kwashiorkor* in Africa) Brock finds it desirable to feed a diet containing 10 per cent fish meal or 18 per cent dried milk: though the possibility of a purely vegetable diet, even in these cases, is upheld by Scrimshaw in Guatemala, who has fed a diet based on cottonseed (*Incaparina*). Both human and animal tests indicate however that leaf protein is to be preferred to seed protein.

It will be shown below that a community at the lowest level of agricultural productivity, living predominantly on cereals, even on coarse cereals such as barley, maize, sorghum or millet, if they have enough calories, will also receive enough protein; though this is not the case with peoples living predominantly on root crops such as cassava, sweet potatoes, yams, or taro.

An attempt to state baldly the average calorie requirements of a population may lead to serious error. Requirements of calories are

---

[1] Dr. Hugh Sinclair, Magdalen College, Oxford, and others; results privately communicated.

functionally related (though not directly proportional) to the weight of the body. They are also influenced by environmental factors — less food is required to maintain body temperature in a warm climate than in a cold one. Active physical work increases calorie requirements, as also do pregnancy and lactation in women.

A population with a high proportion of children (as is the case with most of the populations of Asia and Africa) will simply for that reason require less calories *per head* than a population with a greater percentage of adults. The calculations which follow are based on Table 7, page 45, in the 1957 FAO Report on Calorie Requirements, which relates to such a population, with both birth and death rates fairly high, and a high proportion of children, and of pregnant and lactating women in the population.[1]

Before we proceed to allow for the effects of varying body weights however, we should meet the objection sometimes raised, that these varying body weights themselves are the consequence of varying levels of nutrition. Some make this statement in the extreme form that all differences in body weights throughout the world, from a British policeman down to a central African pygmy, have been so caused, and could be removed by a uniform level of good nutrition — though whether this could be done in a single lifetime, or would require several generations, they do not say; and if they have the latter in mind, they are implying the inheritance of acquired characteristics, which most geneticists regard as a scientifically objectionable proposition.

TABLE I. FOOD CONSUMPTION AND BODY WEIGHTS OF DIFFERENT CASTES IN AN INDIAN VILLAGE

	Average Income Rs./Person/ Month	Food Consumption Calories/ Person/Day	Average Body Weights of Adults Kg. Male	Female
Fishermen	6½	1580	48	41
Harijans (low caste)	7½	1940	46	40
Miscellaneous castes	10	1960	48	41
Agricultural castes	8	2440	49	42
Brahmins and Vaisyas	18	2720	51	45

[1] This table as printed however shows a weighted average requirement for the whole population of 1954 calories, whereas the components add up to 1953 — presumably a misprint.

A very interesting study of a village near the Mysore coast shows the differences which prevail within an Indian community.[1]

We are dealing here with people who have been living, probably for many generations, at violently contrasted levels of income and of nutrition. Between castes the differences in body weight, though discernible, are small in comparison with the differences in weight which prevail between the regions of the world.

In view of the importance of the subject, it is surprising how little information has been collected (that is to say, statistically reliable information, as opposed to impressions based on a few cases) of average heights and weights, even in advanced countries. Information is available regarding the average heights of army recruits in some countries which have *universal* military service (where selective military service prevails, the figures will clearly be biased above the national average). Thus Italian official figures[2] show a steady rise in the average height of 20-year-old conscripts from 162·4 cm (64 ins.) for men born in 1854 to 167·4 cm. for men born in 1929. The contention that this rise can be explained by improved nutrition does not appear very probable in view of the steadiness of the rise, while substantial improvements in the Italian diet did not occur until comparatively recently. Sir Ronald Fisher held that the rise was due to obscure genetic factors slowly working themselves out. Some doctors have contended that this increase only shows that physical maturity is coming earlier, not that the *final* height of Italian men has changed.

Bennett[3] 'has tried, without much success' to assemble what appears to be reliable information on this subject. His list is headed by Montenegrin tribesmen, who are said to have an average height of 182·5 cm. (6 ft.). United States soldiers going to war in 1941–5 had an average weight of 70 kg. and height of 176·5 cm. — these figures should have been only slightly biased by the exclusion of a small number of rejected men. European men appear to average about 65 kg.: the only figure given for Africans (Sudanese) is 57 kg. Latin Americans appear to average 56 kg. Statistics for admissions to prisons in Canton, which should be accurate, though perhaps slightly biased below the average level of the population, give a weight of 49 kg.; most of eastern Asia appears to be within the range 50–55 kg. The African pygmies, at 40 kg.

---

[1] Swaminathan and others, *Indian Journal of Medical Research*, November 1960.

[2] Italian Statistical Abstract (English version), 1954, p. 111.

[3] In *The World's Food*, p. 209.

weight and 140 cm. (55 ins.) height, are separated by a wide margin from all other peoples.

An early Indian study in 1868[1] showed differences between castes comparable with those given above — though the main object of the study was to draw attention to the small size of the Mulchers, a primitive tribe living in the hill forests of Cochin, and subsisting on jungle products.

For men in their twenties, heights and weights were as follows:

	Average Height (cm.)	Average Weight (kg.)
Brahmins	164	53
Other caste Hindus	165	53
Pariahs (untouchables)	165	50
Tank diggers (menial caste)	165	48
Mulchers	152	43

Except for the Mulchers, heights, it will be seen, were similar between the castes; differences seemed to be between what is carried on the bones, not in the bone structure of the body itself.

A still earlier study[2] of 'some rude tribes' of southern India, primitive hunting communities in the jungle, however, gave 48 kg. as the average weight of men, 38 kg. of women.

Likewise the Khyeng, a primitive agricultural community in Burma,[3] showed men of an average weight of 50 kg., women of 43 kg.

The Hanunóo, primitive pagan cultivators in the Philippines classified by ethnologists as 'early Asiatic', show[4] for men an average weight of 48 kg., as with the African pygmies, and height of 153 cm.

Africans on the average appear to be much larger than Asians. McFie in 1956[5] surveyed six villages in Uganda. One village, which shared its country with bands of pygmies, and may have intermarried with them to some extent, had men averaging 52 kg.

[1] G. E. Fryer, 'A Few Words concerning the Hill People inhabiting the Forests of the Cochin State', *Journal of the Royal Asiatic Society*, Vol. 3, 1868.

[2] J. Shortt, 'An Account of some Rude Tribes, the supposed Aborigines of Southern India', *Transactions of the Ethnological Society*, Vol. III, 1865.

[3] G. E. Fryer, 'On the Khyeng People of the Sandoway District', *Journal of the Asiatic Society of Bengal*, Vol. XVIV, Part I, 1875, p. 40.

[4] H. C. Conklin, *Hanunóo Agriculture*, a report on an integral system of shifting cultivation in the Philippines, FAO Forestry Development Paper No. 12, Rome, 1957, p. 10.

[5] J. McFie, Uganda Protectorate Nutrition Surveys, *A Comparison of the Health of Six Villages consuming different types of food*, 1956, p. 23.

(160 cm. height) and women 48 kg. But the other five villages, with widely different food habits, showed men of weight 58–64 kg. (165–175 cm. height) and women 51–59 kg.

We now return to the FAO tables of calorie requirements in different types of community. The adjustments for body weight, and for temperature, have been carefully made, and cannot be improved upon. But the basis from which all the figures are originally calculated is a 'reference man', who appears to be a European weighing 65 kg. and who spends most of his day in a manner rather ambiguously defined, but not apparently working very hard.

As we have some direct information of calorie requirements of Africans in Nigeria working at various tasks[1] it appears preferable to use these as our basis, and also to compute Asian figures from them by adjustments for body weight and temperature; making our own estimates of the proportions of the day devoted to various activities.

It may seem surprising to those not acquainted with Africa, but it appears from all the evidence available (which is discussed in more detail in a later chapter) that the average African at present, subject to periods of intense activity at certain seasons of the year, nevertheless on the average over the year devotes only about four hours per working day to field work. A somewhat higher figure appears to prevail in India, much higher figures in China and the Caribbean. Alternative sets of calculations are given in the table, for men doing four hours' field work a day, and for men doing eight hours' field work a day.

The apportionment of time for the rest of the day is admittedly highly conjectural.

Phillips's experiments were carried out on seven subjects, aged 24 to 33, with weights ranging from 43 to 63 kg., averaging 55 kg. His results for calorie requirements while walking, and in sedentary activities, are used direct in the table below. The sleeping figures are deduced from FAO's 'reference man', with adjustment for body weight and temperature.

For field work, Phillips's figures, adjusted by Trowell,[2] range

---

[1] P. G. Phillips, 'The Metabolic Cost of Common West African Agricultural Activities', *Journal of Tropical Medicine and Hygiene*, London, 1954, Vol. 57, No. 12. Phillips computed calorie requirements per hour from the rate of oxygen consumption as measured by the Douglas bag.

[2] H. C. Trowell, 'Calorie and Protein Requirements of Adult Male Africans', *East African Medical Journal*, May 1955, Vol. 32, No. 5, p. 156.

from 213 calories/hour for carrying a log of 20 kg., to 269 for grass cutting, 274 for hoeing, the principal agricultural activity of Africans, 360 for sawing, 372 for bush clearing, and 504 for tree felling. It is well known, however, that men engaged in extremely arduous tasks such as the latter cannot work continuously. The FAO calorie report quotes (page 59) an estimate by Lehmann to the effect that men engaged in such work, if they are to preserve their health, must be allowed rest pauses, which bring their overall average for calorie consumption down to 300 per hour. Converting to African body weight, and reducing slightly, we take a figure of 250 calories/hour for requirements while working.

The adjustment of FAO's European 'reference man' to African conditions gives a requirement of 2707 calories/day; whereas our own calculations direct from African data raise this figure to 2820, even at the present rate of working, or 3402 if an eight-hour day is to be worked. These latter figures form the basis for the calculations for the other regions shown in the table. The reader's attention is drawn to the table of weights at the end of the book.

An attempt was made also to estimate the way in which the average African woman spent her day, and consequently her calorie requirements. Even after allowing however for the amount of field work, and heavy housework such as pounding grain and carrying water, done by the African woman, the result came out very little different from that obtained by starting with the European 'reference woman', and converting for African body weight and temperature. Apparently the FAO physiologists credited the European woman with a good deal of heavy housework; at any rate she cleans and manages a much larger house than the African woman.

Estimates of calorie requirements were also made, as shown in the table, for India and south-east Asia, and for southern and northern China — regions which, with Africa, include a large proportion of all the world's subsistence cultivators. The average body weights however had to be fairly arbitrarily assumed. The average temperatures also were only approximately estimated from examination of the maps of isotherms.

In the following table, the 'components, of the average for the whole community of calorie requirements per head, e.g. for children computed from the average requirements per child multiplied by the proportion of the population constituted by children, add up to a correctly weighted average for the population as a whole.

TABLE II. CALORIES REQUIREMENTS OF A 'YOUNG' POPULATION WITH HIGH BIRTH AND DEATH RATES

	Assumed body weights of adults kg. — Men	Women	Temperature C°	Calories/day required by men aged 20-29 — hr/day	cal/hr	cal/day	hr/day	cal/hr	cal/day	Children under 15 (temperature only)	Women	Men (4 h)	Men (8 h)	Total (4 h)	Total (8 h)
FAO estimates	50	40	25			2445				727	447	779		1953	
Do. converted for African weight	57½	—	25			2707									
Central Africa [a]	57½	50	25							727	526	897	1084	2150	2337
Field work				4	250	1000	8	250	2000						
Other active work and recreation (e.g. housebuilding, dancing)				1	250	250	1	250	250						
Walking				2	184	368	1	184	184						
Sedentary activities				9	78	702	6	78	468						
Sleeping				8	62½	500	8	62½	500						
						2820			3402						
India, S.E. Asia	50	40	25			2545			3070	727	447	811	978	1985	2152
Southern China	50	40	20			2614			3153	747	459	834	1003	2040	2209
Northern China	55	45	10			2735			3300	786	528	871	1051	2185	2365

[a] Revised estimates based on African experience.

We have some information about the calorie value of food consumption in low-income communities, computed both from national averages and from field studies. Outstanding among the latter is the classical study by Buck, *Land Utilization in China*.[1] In the late 1920s, China was enjoying a brief respite of ordered government. A Department of Agricultural Economics, under Buck's direction, was established at the University of Nanking, and endowed from American sources with adequate resources for research. After a period of training, over a thousand Chinese students were sent back each to his own native village, where he spoke the dialect and understood the people, to spend a whole year in the village recording crops, sales, food consumption, and much more information. As a result, we know more about the agricultural economy of China in the 1930s than we do about any other low-income agricultural economy (except the Japanese) even to this day. Out of these thousand or so villages, Buck made a dietary survey for 136. He measured calories per adult male unit; converted to calories per head of population (from data given by him) the average for China in the 1930s works out at 2533 per day, a food supply well above minimum requirements. There are however strong regional differences; in the winter wheat/millet area calorie consumption was only 2240/person/day, which is inadequate for a cold climate for large-bodied people. The 136 surveys were almost equally divided between northern and southern (rice region) China. Taking the standards given in the above table (which are higher than the 2154 calories/person/day which Buck proposed as a minimum standard) we find the following percentages of all villages surveyed below requirements during the year of survey:

	Northern China	Southern China
Below 60% of requirements	3	—
60– 70% ,, ,,	10	1
70– 80% ,, ,,	12	3
80– 90% ,, ,,	13	6
90–100% ,, ,,	13	7
Above requirements	49	83
	100	100

Some of the villages however were consuming food at a rate more than twice requirements. These marked differences between vil-

[1] *Land Utilization in China*, Nanking, 1937.

lages indicate, amongst other things, the lack of transport, and also the great variability of harvests. One can only hope that it is not the same villages which are hungry year by year.

For Communist China, the best available information indicates that, except for the single year 1958, when the harvest was unusually good, food consumption per head has been substantially below the level of the 1930s.

In the *Yearbook of Food and Agricultural Statistics* published by FAO a table is given showing the protein and calorie content of the average diets of certain countries. Contrary to the usual trend, the countries for which information is now published constitute a much shorter list than that which was published a few years ago; this is a tacit admission that much of the previous information was highly inaccurate. It is necessary to mention this, because many readers may still have some of the earlier published figures, now abandoned, in their minds. For instance, in the early 1950s some very low figures were quoted of Indian grain output and calorie supply per head, and many people still think in terms of these figures. During this period, however, when there was a widespread prevalence, or at any rate threat, of compulsory state purchase of grain, there was every inducement for the cultivator to understate his grain output, so as to avoid compulsory purchase, to leave himself some grain for sale on the black market, or possibly even to qualify for a ration himself. The official estimates were almost certainly understated. In 1947 one of the writers had a most illuminating conversation on this subject with Gandhi, who was very interested in economics. He pointed out what was happening, and strongly criticized Mr. Nehru's policy. Drop rationing and price control, he said, and every Indian would have to work harder, which he could well do. Nobody but Gandhi would have been so frank on this subject.

On the other hand, the willingness of the Indian Government over this period to devote foreign exchange, which was badly needed for other purposes, to the purchase of grain, shows that it considered the situation dangerous.

Most of the countries for which information is now published by FAO are economically advanced countries in which there is no question of a lack of calories. Among the low figures entered is one of 2210 calories for Japanese consumption, which might at first sight appear to be barely adequate. In Japan, however, people willingly devote a substantial proportion of their food expenditure to fish, fruit, vegetables and other products whose calorific return is comparatively low per unit of money spent; they would not do this if they were hungry. The average Japanese body weight is still low (though now found among school children to be rising rapidly)[1] and, for a temperature which can be taken as intermediate between that of northern China and southern China, a diet of this calorific value would appear to be adequate. A figure for Japan of 2310 was found in a study by the United States Department of Agriculture (see below).

The figure now given by FAO for India is 1950 calories per head (2050 in the U.S. Department of Agriculture study). Though Indian agricultural statistics are improving, no one well acquainted with the subject could say that they are yet precise. Good field studies in India are still scarce. Recently an enquiry was started, under international auspices, with a view to making fully detailed records of food production and consumption in certain selected villages.[2] Surveys were made in twelve villages, spread over areas of four different soil types, which showed the following average consumption of calories per head per day:

Well-drained loam with irrigation	2141
Stiff black clay	2018
Poorly drained clay	2005
Poor sandy soil	1853

Average requirements for India, even for a four-hour working day, were thus not met in one district; for an eight-hour working day, in none of them.

Another study on average calorie intake throughout Asia, Africa and Latin America was recently completed by the United States Department of Agriculture.[3] In a number of cases they come out with figures significantly higher than those of FAO. In one calculation they find a large number of countries below what they state to be the minimum level of calorie requirements: but this was after allowing, not only for milling and storage losses of grain, but also

[1] The Japanese Education Ministry, after checking 5 million students, reported that 12-year-old boys and girls were $\frac{1}{2}$ in. taller and 2 lb. heavier than those of the same age in 1936. The average Japanese of 12 is now 4 ft. 8 in. tall and weighs 75 lb. The Ministry attributed the growth to improved diet (*New York Times*, 24 June 1957).

[2] L. D. Stamp, *Geographical Review*, New York, January 1958, quoting work by Shafi, referring to villages in the eastern part of the state of Uttar Pradesh, in the years 1953 to 1956.

[3] U.S.D.A., FAS-M 101, 104, 108, Parts II, III and IV. *Food Balances in Other Countries*, Washington, 1960–61.

for an assumed further 15 per cent wastage in consumption. It does not seem reasonable to assume that really hungry people would waste so much food.

Their results may be classified as follows (omitting countries which are clearly nowhere near the bread line):

TABLE III. AVERAGE CALORIE INTAKE — AFRICA, ASIA, LATIN AMERICA

AFRICA (standard 2150 on basis of 4-hour day)

Tunisia	2170	Rest of former French West Africa	2450
Tanganyika	2175	Cameroons	2470
Libya	2180	Morocco	2480
Angola	2215	Rhodesia-Nyasaland	2500
Algeria	2230	Liberia	2540
Kenya	2240	Former French Equatorial Africa	2575
Ethiopia	2295	Ghana	2605
Sudan	2295	Togo	2645
Egypt	2340	Congo	2650
Guinea	2400	Nigeria	2680

ASIA (standard 1985 on basis of 4-hour day)

Pakistan	2030	Jordan	2085
South Korea	2040	Indonesia	2125
Iran	2040	Philippines	2145
India	2050	Burma	2150
Ceylon	2060	Thailand	2185

(standard 2152 on basis of 8-hour day)

Syria	2225	Japan	2310
Iraq	2255	Lebanon	2415
Malaya	2290	Taiwan	2430

LATIN AMERICA (assumed standard 2200)

Haiti	1875	Guatemala	2175
Bolivia	1880	Honduras	2190
Ecuador	1935	Colombia	2225
Dominican Republic	1950	Venezuela	2255
El Salvador	1975	Paraguay	2355
Nicaragua	1985	Panama	2370
Peru	2040	Costa Rica	2555

The African (except for Tunisia) and Asian figures look probable; but the Latin American figures look improbably low.

If people's food falls short of their calorie requirements it does not follow that they die. They may indeed live for years on end on an inadequate diet. Resistance to many kinds of illness however is indubitably weakened, and both sickness and mortality are much greater than they would be if the community were better fed. The FAO experts describe what happens in such a community — 'The whole manner of life is adapted to an insufficient supply of calories, with results that are socially undesirable: lack of drive and initiative; avoidance of physical and mental effort; excessive rest.'

We can recognize these symptoms in some present and past communities. Quite a widespread phenomenon is 'pre-harvest hunger'. The variations of food intake, and of the changes in body weight which accompany them, were measured by Culwick[1] in a dietary survey among the Zande of the south-western Sudan. Calorie intake curves and weight trends were high after the main harvest, declining towards the end of the dry season, and falling sharply at the beginning of the new agricultural season.

TABLE IV.   ZANDE CALORIE INTAKE CURVES AND WEIGHT TRENDS

	Average Body Weight		Average Calorie Intake	Average Protein Intake
	men kg.	women kg.	cals./head/day	g./head/day
First harvest	54·5	49·5	2,275	41
Main harvest	56·5	49·0	2,775	60
Dry season	57·5	50·5	2,400	56
Beginning of new agricultural season	56·0	50·5	1,925	33
Mean heights cm.	167·5	157·5		

The community were obviously eating above requirements at certain seasons, though at lowest levels of intake they appear to have received an inadequate supply of calories. On the other hand, the extensive system of axe and hoe agriculture practised by this peasant group left them access to a wide range of wild products. It is well known that nutritional surveys have not taken account of snacks and nibblings apart from main meals. Children penetrate far into the bush in search of wild fruits, and men and women certainly consume wild products while at work clearing food farms. Time spent foraging may in fact constitute part of the reason for the low number of hours actually spent on clearing.

[1] G. M. Culwick, *A Dietary Survey among the Zande of the South-western Sudan*, Ministry of Agriculture, Sudan Government, 1950.

In general people were gaining weight during the latter half of the rainy season, from the maize harvest onwards, and losing during the dry season, when qualitative observations showed that their feeding was ragged and haphazard. Culwick emphasizes that the overall pattern hides a great deal of individual variation, and that individual circumstances readily overrode the general seasonal trend. She saw people 'put on years in age or go haggard in a few weeks, and some months later they would hardly be recognizable as they shed their apparent years, rounded out again in body and restored their usual manner of living'. Signs of stress were reflected in not bothering, or not being able, to prepare and cook proper meals, and the general impression was one of a precariously maintained balance between a state of relative wellbeing and states of stress, complex in both origin and manifestation. Abbott, who carried out a clinical survey of Culwick's group, draws attention to the dearth of knowledge of African dietary requirements, and states that due cognizance must be taken of the parasites which the African supports.

Arising out of a study of growth and mortality in children in an African village, McGregor[1] came to the conclusion that infectious disease and inadequate maternal care are probably the major factors contributing to high mortality and impaired growth in young children, and that malnutrition seems to be more often secondary to disease than primary.

A survey made in 1950 showed that malaria was hyperendemic, the crude parasite rate for all ages being 54·7 per cent; that approximately 36 per cent and 33 per cent of villagers were carriers of microfilariae of *wuchereria bancrofti* and *anopheles perstans* respectively; that 2·5 per cent of the population were suffering from trypanosomiasis; and that hookworm and ascaris infections abounded. Against this background of varied and heavy parasitization there was a recurrent shortage of harvested cereals, although inadequate supplies were reinforced by extensive collection of bush fruits, nuts, berries, and green leaves.

In India, faecal-borne illnesses are the most formidable problems, now that the incidence of malaria has been greatly reduced by eradication programmes. Intestinal infestation by worms is widespread, of which hookworm is the most important. Intestinal parasites offer a strong competition to the human body in metabolizing

---

[1] I. A. McGregor, 'Growth and Mortality in Children in an African Village', *British Medical Journal*, 23 December 1961.

food. The economic loss from deaths occuring from faecal-borne diseases, as well as from the illnesses with attendant disability and lowered productivity, continues to be serious in rural India.

Preoccupation of women with their crops was given as the reason for a fall in calorie intake at certain times of the year in Northern Rhodesia by Thomson,[1] who studied a group of cultivating families. Although grain may be plentiful, when they were engaged on certain agricultural operations the women only returned to the village in the evening to cook. She observed, however, that the men were probably getting a fairly adequate diet, and that the group that suffered most were the women, though she admits that 'cook's titbits' taken from the pot may have been considerable. Typical of such communities is the heavy dependence on a starchy staple. She states a strong case for higher intakes of animal foods, since they contain a better ratio of essential amino acids than those derived from vegetable sources. Even in Japan however the weight of meat, eggs and milk in the diet of farm families is small, amounting to only 4 per cent of their total protein intake. Japanese farmers are heavy eaters with 80 per cent of their total calorie intake coming from cereals, mainly rice. Intake of proteins averages about 63 g./day, almost entirely from vegetable sources.

In Africa, maldistribution may arise with younger members of the family, and lactating women, who are eating the same low-protein high-calorie food, but are unable to do so in sufficient quantity to meet their protein requirements.

Greater dangers arise when primitive cultivators change from one staple to another. Gourou[2] warns that protein shortages increase with the spread of manioc cultivation (also known as cassava, or tapioca, and which is poorer in protein than yam or millet). Pulses can however be grown on relatively dry and infertile soils, which not only increase the fertility of the soil, but have a high protein content and are good sources of minerals and vitamins of the B group. Their proteins supplement rice proteins, and a greater intake of pulses is easier to bring about than an increase in the consumption of meat, milk or eggs.

One supposed consequence of inadequate feeding can be denied categorically, namely the fantastic claim by De Castro that it increases fertility. The evidence for underfeeding increasing fertility

---

[1] B. P. Thomson, *Two Studies in African Nutrition*, Rhodes-Livingstone Paper No. 24, Manchester University Press, 1954, pp. 49, 51.
[2] P. Gourou, *The Tropical World*, 3rd ed. 1961, p.74.

in animals which De Castro adduces is uncertain enough: his supposed evidence for this happening among humans is ridiculous. Such evidence as we have[1] indicates that the natural fertility (when not artificially impeded) of Europeans is higher than that of Asians and Africans.

De Castro finds a good deal of hunger in his own country, Brazil, which has now been responsible for running its own affairs for a very long time; nevertheless, he tries to prove that anything wrong in Brazil is still the result of 'colonialism'. He makes no proposals for agricultural reforms, apart from the adoption of Lysenko's ideas on genetics, which he greatly favours; so far as he proposes anything, it seems to be greater reliance upon primitive rather than on commercial agriculture.

In any plans for remedying the considerable actual hunger, and widespread low diets with threat of hunger, which prevail in the world, it must be the improvement of agriculture in the poorer communities (representing a preponderant proportion of the earth's inhabitants) which principally receives attention.

Some readers may be disappointed. Are there no plans, they may ask, for producing even more food in the countries which already find their abundant productivity embarrassing — United States, Canada, Australasia, possibly Western Europe — and distributing it among the poorer communities?

Such plans have indeed been discussed. The difficulties which they will encounter will not be predominantly economic, however, but of a diplomatic and political nature. The present government of China, for instance, when approached by the International Red Cross — the most non-political approach possible — with an offer of gifts of food, promptly denied that anyone was short of food in China. India has accepted some food from the United States — but has almost made a favour of doing so. With Asia and Africa as they are now, full of newly-formed countries neurotically pre-occupied with the concept of 'independence', we must expect that most governments will be unwilling to admit that there is anything wrong with their food supply, or to accept gifts of food.

And, moreover, an economic problem arises too, in respect of the really poor and backward communities, who live a great distance away from railways, roads, shops, government offices and the like.

[1] See Sauvy, *Population*, October-December 1953, on Japanese fertility; and W. Brass, *The estimation of total fertility rates from data for primitive communities*, World Population Conference 1954, on African fertility.

These people live perforce almost entirely on food which they can produce in their own villages; and will have to continue to do so until methods of transport and distribution are greatly improved. An attempt to feed them on imported food, generously donated by governments at the other end of the world, would raise very serious transport and distribution problems. Lacking other means of transport, loads of food would have to be carried for long distances on men's heads.

In any case, prudent statesmen, both in the giving and in the receiving countries, recognize that such gifts of food, even when they can be organized, should be regarded only as a strictly temporary measure. They must not be allowed in any way to delay the urgent task of helping the peoples of the poorer countries to produce more food for themselves (or, in a few cases, other products which they can exchange for food in the world market). A state of permanent dependence is not desired by either party.

CHAPTER II

Pre-Agricultural Man

Biologists used to tell us that the human race has been in existence on this earth for half a million years. More recently, they have been telling us that remains of what were obviously genuine humans can be dated a million years back — though how the dating is done is not precisely explained, and indeed biologists seem so casual over the whole matter that one sometimes wonders whether they have even got the right number of zeroes.

Whether its duration has been a million or half a million years, it remains true that by far the greatest part of the whole time which the human race has spent on this earth — though the number of people living in those distant aeons was far, far smaller than the numbers living now — has been passed in communities living solely by hunting, fishing and the gathering of wild products, without any knowledge of, or need for agriculture: and a few such communities survive to this day.

We should not idealize primitive life, the life of the 'noble savage', which made such an appeal to jaded eighteenth-century aristocrats and literary men (making up most of their facts to please themselves, because they were almost entirely lacking in knowledge about the actual life of such peoples). But we need not go to the other extreme, and commiserate unduly with our ancestors for the life which they lived — least of all should we believe the wild fictions about cave men, which are still written up as scientific knowledge for children's textbooks. Conditions of primitive hunting peoples must not be judged, wrote Carl Sauer,[1] 'from their modern survivors, now restricted to the most meagre regions of the earth, such as the interior of Australia, the American Great Basin, and the Arctic tundra and taiga. The areas of early occupation were abounding in food.'

We should therefore imagine our ancestors living in warm forest and grasslands where game, fuel and water were abundant. It was perhaps only in comparatively recent times that they found such

[1] *Geographical Review*, January 1947, Vol. IV, p. 263.

land pre-empted, by agricultural communities or by other hunters, and were compelled to make their homes in the colder and more arid regions of the world. It is true that their lives were not long — the evidence of the burial grounds shows that a man of forty was a rarity in the palaeolithic world — but a life in the open air, subsisting entirely on game and fish caught by oneself, must have been very attractive to able-bodied young men — at any rate if we judge from the large sums which wealthy men are willing to spend in order to enjoy a few days' fishing or shooting in remote surroundings, in the nearest replica of primitive conditions which it is possible to create at the present time.

With high mortality rates, however, due to accidents in the hunting field, and the inability of such communities to give any support to ill or infirm people, the rate of population growth was almost negligibly slow — had it not been, the world would have passed through the hunting and fishing stage, and reached the agricultural stage, far quicker than it in fact did.

Not long ago, archaeologists were unable to reach, within very wide limits, any valid conclusions about the places and times of the origin of agriculture. The discovery of the method of radio-carbon dating for archaeological remains however has thrown a flood of light on this problem during recent years. The evidence, conveniently summarized by Cipolla,[1] shows that the oldest known agricultural settlement was where some springs of water provide natural irrigation for the hot dry land at Jericho, dated about 7000 B.C. Although no doubt there are many further discoveries yet in store, nevertheless judging from the way in which subsequent sites appear to spread outwards from it, it is quite possible that there is something in the traditional belief that the Middle East was the original cradle of civilization. Within 500 years of the original known agricultural settlement in Jericho, agriculture was being practised in Kurdistan. Within a little more than another 500 years pastoralists were grazing domestic animals on the southern shore of the Caspian Sea. The oldest agriculture in the Nile valley appears to have been about 4500 B.C. By 3300 B.C. agriculture had spread to what is now the extremely arid area of Baluchistan (Western Pakistan). But as early as 3650 B.C. agriculture had reached the western hemisphere, and maize was being grown in New Mexico. Whether this knowledge was brought by sea travellers across the Pacific, or by nomads crossing the Bering Straits, or was indepen-

[1] C. M. Cipolla, *The Economic History of World Population*, Penguin, 1962.

dently discovered, is not known. By 2200 B.C. maize growing was
being practised in Peru. By 3000 B.C. agriculture had penetrated
Africa as far south as Kenya.

The requirements of living space of pre-agricultural man may be
considerable. For a community living entirely by hunting, fishing,
and the gathering of any wild fruits or roots which may be going,
we must expect to record population densities, not in persons per
sq. km., but in sq. km. per person. Nougier[1] estimated that the
inhabitants of Australia before the coming of white settlers had
about 30 sq. km. per head to hunt over,[2] and it was generally agreed
that they did not have much to spare.

In Tasmania, with good rainfall and abundant fishing, in comparison with the Australian mainland, the native population (still
at the palaeolithic stage of culture at the arrival of the white man)
was estimated[3] at 4000, i.e. 17 sq. km./person. A most interesting
account[4] of the South Island of New Zealand shows that about the
thirteenth century, when the country was inhabited by the Moriori,
and the moa (large flightless birds) were there for them to hunt,
population density was 10–15 sq. km./person: but by the eighteenth century, after the moa had been exterminated by the hunters, and the Moriori had been exterminated by the Maori in-
vaders, density was down to a figure of over 30 sq. km./person.

In a cold climate the Eskimos and Indians of north-western
Canada now require 140 sq. km. per head. Grahame Clark[5] thinks
that space requirements per man range from 80 to 500 sq. km. per
head in sub-arctic lands. Rätzel[6] quotes a figure between 40 and
90 sq. km. for temperate climates. Childe[7] gave a figure distinctly
higher than Nougier's (over 40 sq. km.) for land requirements per
head of the Australian aborigines; but points out that this figure
may fall in better provided regions, to 20–25 on the American
prairies and as low as 10 in the warm humid climate of the Pacific
coast of North America. Under particularly favourable conditions,
as on the shores of rivers which enjoy a regular run of salmon, the

[1] *Population*, Paris, April–June 1954.
[2] It is a mistake to imagine, as is commonly supposed, that the whole interior
of Australia is desert. The area of true desert is very limited. A very large part of
the country is semi-arid, which is quite a different thing. Such country will
support fairly abundant game.
[3] Krzywicki, *Primitive Society and its Vital Statistics*, p. 59.
[4] Cumberland, *Geographical Review*, April 1962.
[5] Grahame Clark, *Archaeology and Society*, 2nd ed., London, 1947.
[6] Quoted by Taylor, *Canadian Journal of Economics and Political Science*,
August 1950.
[7] G. Childe, *What Happened in History*, Penguin, 1954.

figure may fall to 1·5. Sauer also estimates less than $2\frac{1}{2}$ sq. km./ person as the potentiality of the best lands occupied by primitive peoples. Under these conditions, he thinks, they are likely to combine in groups of 6 to 12 families to hunt and collect over an area of 80 to 100 sq. km. (i.e. a radius of about 5 km.) with a permanent central camp site; and so we have the beginnings of civilization. This estimate of 5 km. radius is only for the best hunting and fishing land; if we assume a community of 50 people and an average space requirement of 10 sq. km./person, the radius of the settlement becomes $12\frac{1}{2}$ km. The formation of a settlement has to be, Sauer pointed out, a careful economic decision; to try to organize hunting over too great an area involves an uneconomic amount of travelling to and from the camp site.

It was under such conditions, Childe thought, that the people of the Magdalenian period were living in Europe, originally in the open air: they took to caves when the climate suddenly became colder. It appears that they were able to organize quite an active social life; at any rate they left us some magnificent paintings.

Primitive agriculture (which may come before the domestication of animals) reduces space requirements down to something between 1 and 5 sq. km./person, according to Rätzel. With the domestication of animals this figure falls to $\frac{1}{2}$. By the time people are living in settled villages, and really taking agriculture seriously, the figure may go on falling down to 0·15.

Domestication of animals — in this case the reindeer — greatly improves the population-carrying capacity of the Arctic too. Soviet scientists[1] have estimated that one reindeer can live on the grazing from 0·6 to 1 sq. km., so that a tribe living on the milk and meat of reindeer, and on fish, should only require a few sq. km. per person.

The largest Neolithic village found anywhere, Cipolla points out, had only three to four hundred inhabitants. Assuming 10 km. as the radius over which people are able to travel for food-producing activities (and this is a high assumption), this gives the community an area of 314 sq. km. for this purpose, a little below 1 sq. km./person. We can see therefore that communities even of this size, which seems very small to us, are only possible when the agricultural arts have advanced beyond the most primitive stage, and probably include the domestication of animals.

---

[1] V. N. Andreev and Z. P. Savkina, *International Grassland Conference*, Reading, 1960, p. 166.

Nougier drew his conclusions from burial grounds, and from the ratio between palaeolithic and neolithic remains. The palaeolithic inhabitants of France were quite comfortably off with 55 sq. km. of space per head (i.e. only 10,000 population for the whole of France). Neolithic France however, as early as 2000 B.C., still using stone implements, though more skilfully shaped than those of the palaeolithic men, without any bronze or iron, was living according to Nougier at a density of 0·1 sq. km. per head, i.e. the whole country was carrying a population of 5 million. Many French writers however hold that this was the population of Gaul at the time it was invaded by Julius Caesar; if this is so, there must have been a long preceding period of population stagnation. But even if the population in 2000 B.C. was half or less of Nougier's estimate, it still follows that it must have been, by the standards of that time, a dense population, already dependent upon comparatively advanced agricultural techniques.

Palaeolithic Britain, according to Nougier, was inhabited only by 'some hundreds or thousands'. Only the Thames valley was fully occupied. Grahame Clark is more specific. Early palaeolithic Britain, he considers, had a permanent population of only about 250, but may have had some summer visitors from Europe. By the mesolithic period he gives Britain a population of three to four thousand[1] with an average of 65 sq. km. per head, or fairly comfortable living room. Neolithic Britain had a population of 20 thousand (12 sq. km. per head) and Middle Bronze Age Britain 30 to 40 thousand. Most of these were in England, where they had less than 5 sq. km. of hunting ground per head, and really had to begin to think about agriculture. In Scotland, according to Childe, there were still only 2,500 people in the Early Bronze Age, with an average of 30 sq. km. per head, still able to live by hunting.

At some time between 3000 B.C. and 2000 B.C., even if the amount of land were still 12 sq. km. per head when Scotland was taken into account, higher densities of population were prevailing in the south, and it became necessary to practise agriculture, the art of which was probably acquired from Gaul.

With neolithic agriculture, the population of England continued to grow, though its density was still much less than in Gaul. The invasion of the Belgae (though there is some dispute about this) is said to have introduced the heavy wheeled plough, which made

[1] This estimate is confirmed by Professor H. J. Fleure, *Geographical Review*, October 1945.

possible the cultivation of the clay soils in which Britain abounds (the first British agriculturists had to confine themselves to the cultivation of light sandy soils). By this time, Grahame Clark estimates that population had risen to 400 thousand, mostly in England and Wales rather than in Scotland, i.e. a density of $\frac{1}{2}$ sq. km. or less per person.

The land which now constitutes the United States and Canada has a total area of 17 million sq. km., or 14 million if we deduct the tundra; perhaps a further small deduction should be made for completely arid land. In the sixteenth century, at the time of the arrival of the white man, this area had a population of one million.[1] The North American Indians too about that time were facing their 'population crisis', and were beginning to find it necessary to change over to agriculture. Agriculture in Mexico and Peru, as we have seen above, had been in existence for thousands of years, and had made great civilizations possible. Geographers believe that it is possible to trace the spread, about this time, of maize growing up the valleys from Mexico, while the higher ground remained occupied by hunting peoples.

By the latter part of the seventeenth century, travellers and settlers in New England had acquired considerable knowledge of the means of livelihood of the American Indians there. A careful survey makes possible an interesting estimate of the sources of food supply of a people who were in transition from hunting to an agricultural economy. This transition towards agriculture by this time, however, judging from the proportion of their calories which it supplied, was two-thirds completed.

The following table gives M. K. Bennett's compilation[2] of the diet of American Indians in New England in the first three-quarters of the seventeenth century, as recorded by a large number of contemporaries.

While population growth appears to have been the motive force compelling our ancestors, and others (possibly with great reluctance at the time) to abandon the hunting life for the agricultural, there is an interesting possibility that this process may occasionally go into reverse. The disappearance of the Norse community in Greenland about the fourteenth century is an event which undoubtedly took place, though its causes are much debated. Some

[1] A. Landry, *Traité de Démographie*, Paris, 1949; Vanzetti, Società Italiana di Sociologia Rurale, *Land and Man in Latin America*, 1961.
[2] *Journal of Political Economy*, October 1955.

hold that wars, or epidemics, aggravated by a worsening of the climate, are sufficient explanation; but Stefansson, who knows the country well, holds that the Greenlanders, cut off from contact with Europe by the King of Norway's commercial monopoly, found a hunting and fishing life more congenial than working on their agricultural settlements, and after a short time intermarried with and became indistinguishable from Eskimos. In the substantial depopulation of Britain which appears to have occurred in the fifth and sixth centuries A.D. the inhabitants of some areas also probably reverted to a hunting life.

TABLE V. AVERAGE DIET OF AMERICAN INDIANS
MEASURED IN CALORIES PER HEAD PER DAY

	U.S. 1952	American Indians (New England) 1605–1675
Grain	740	1625 –
Meat and poultry	700	250 +
Milk and milk products	512	
Sugar	500	
Vegetable fats and oils	274	25 –
Vegetables and fruits	210	100
Tubers	94	50 –
Nuts and legume seeds	94	200 +
Eggs	90	25 –
Fish and shellfish	13	225
Cocoa and chocolate	13	
	3240	2500

To this day it is still possible to find truly nomadic peoples living on meat, fish, and wild seeds and roots, though anthropologists will have to hurry: they have not many more years in which to make their records and measurements, before such communities become sophisticated, and begin to obtain their food supplies from elsewhere.

In 1941 Holmberg[1] successfully measured the quantities of meat consumed daily by the Siriono — a group of semi-nomadic hunters and food gatherers inhabiting an extensive tropical area of eastern Bolivia. No clothing of any kind is manufactured or worn by the Siriono; they hunt wild game with bows and arrows. Unlike many of their South American Indian contemporaries, who have developed or adopted methods of trapping fish, they also do all

[1] Smithsonian Institute of Social Anthropology, Publication No. 10, 1950.

their fishing with the bow and arrow, a factor which limits their fishing activities to the dry season, when rivers and lakes are low and the waters are clear.

Meat is the most desired item in the diet of these Indians. Holmberg attached himself to a band of about 50 adults, and kept records of the amount of game hunted and consumed for a period of three months. No meat was being introduced from outside. Per head of the total population of the tribe meat consumption appeared to be at the rate of only 0·22 kg./day. Even allowing for a large margin of error, the average Siriono eats at the most 125 kg./year of meat obtained from hunting with bows and arrows, equivalent to about 850 calories/person/day.

In the Siriono economy, collecting ranks next to hunting in importance, particularly of wild fruits and wild honey. Small plots of mixed garden crops are invariably planted during the semi-sedentary rainy season when the waters of the numerous lakes and rivers of the area are still too high to allow extensive migration, and meat supplies are reduced; they seldom sow plots of any size as they are often not at hand to reap the harvest. Eating habits depend largely upon quantities of food available for consumption at the moment. Holmberg records that when food is plentiful people eat to excess and do little else. It is not uncommon for four people to eat a peccary weighing 27 kg. at a sitting. When meat is plentiful, a man has been known to consume 13 kg. within 24 hours. But when food is scarce they go hungry while looking for something more to eat. He emphasizes, however, that though the supply of food is rarely abundant and always insecure, starvation does not occur.

Still more primitive — and voracious — are the Bushmen of South West Africa. 'The Bushmen,[1] a remnant of the original inhabitants of Africa, may still be found — the last of primitive man. They do not cultivate the soil; the men hunt with bows and poisoned arrows; the women and children wander far afield in search of roots, leaves and berries. Hunger compels them to eat everything that is edible — buck, hyena, leopard, snakes, birds, frogs, locusts, grasshoppers, flying ants; they have an intimate knowledge of wild products, and know exactly where and at what time of the year they will find particular foods. They are prodigious eaters when they are fortunate enough to kill a large animal. Men weighing no more than 45 kg. (7 stone) will consume at one sitting

[1] M. R. Haswell, 'Economics and Population in Africa', *The Month*, November 1960.

up to twenty times the quantity of food which would normally be eaten by a settled cultivator; they have a remarkable elasticity of stomach. Thrust back by frontier contacts to live under the harsh climatic conditions of the Kalahari Desert where temperatures can change overnight from quite severe frosts to 35° C during the day, their numbers have dwindled to a mere 15–16,000. Communities living by hunting and food gathering require very large areas of land per person merely to subsist, and under the near-arid conditions of the Kalahari where there is nothing but damp sand from which to procure water — skilfully sucked through a hollow reed and transferred for storage to ostrich egg-shells — density of population is as low as 300 sq. km. (approximately 120 sq.m.)/person.'

Further ideas on the food supply of pre-agricultural man are given by Pirie.[1] On an area of 20 sq. km. (which we have taken above as about the area required to support one person in grassland country), and taking the median of the four separate estimates which Pirie quotes, we must conclude that the stock of game animals is about 130 tons liveweight. Small game may reproduce itself very rapidly; let us however make the unfavourable assumption that this game consists only of large, slow-breeding animals, reproducing themselves on the average only every three years. This area then still yields 40 tons liveweight of meat per year. An active population, requiring 2500 calories per person per day, and living entirely on meat (they would have an excessive intake of protein, which would be excreted without harming them), and assuming that they are not so fastidious as we are about consuming tripes and heads, etc., would require, however, only one ton of game, measured liveweight, per head per year.

Does the primitive hunter really require a forty-fold margin over his requirements? It appears that he does. Most of the game, in fact, is eaten by wild predatory animals; man cannot hope to extirpate them, or even keep them in check, until his own numbers have substantially increased. Skilful though primitive hunters have been in devising bows and arrows, boomerangs, etc., and in tracking large animals, they often have to work hard actually to kill them. Finally, there is the important point that when they do catch a large animal they have no means of preserving it and, in spite of the feats of trenchermanship which they perform, a large proportion of the meat is bound to be wasted.

[1] *Journal of the Royal Statistical Society*, Series A, Vol. 125, Part 3, 1962.

CHAPTER III

Primitive and Shifting Agriculture[1]

That care and feeling for the distant past, which have shown themselves in many striking results obtained by Danish archaeologists, led Jørgensen[2] to try an experiment reproducing, so far as possible, the conditions under which the pioneers of agriculture in Denmark worked. A group of students volunteered to clear and burn, with primitive tools, the sort of scrubland (lacking heavy tree growth) which is believed to have prevailed in large parts of Denmark at that time. They were forcibly reminded of one drawback with which pioneers of agriculture in hitherto uncultivated areas to-day in Africa and Australia are all to familiar, namely that every bird for miles around considers that these new edible seeds were planted for his benefit. The Danish volunteers put in much time bird-scaring, but nevertheless still obtained a very poor harvest. For clearing the land, with primitive iron tools, it was found that they worked at the rate of 245 man-hours/ha. cleared. Clearing which still leaves the big stumps in the ground[3] calls for 37 man-day/ha., cleared (probably only about 200 man-hours, as the working day is short). Beckett[4] from experience in Ghana estimates that the clearing of heavy forest calls for 50–75 man-day/ha., even when the big trees are left (in any case, cocoa farmers may find them useful for shade); for re-clearing secondary bush, 25–37 man-day/ha.; but clearing the open savannah in the drier climates, rather than the thick rain forest, requires 10–20 man-days/ha. only.

Present-day Africans presumably have sharper axes than iron age cultivators in Denmark; at the same time, they have more abundant scrub growth to clear. For bronze-age cultivators the task would have been heavier, and for the first agriculturists, using

---

[1] Grateful acknowledgement is made to the Leverhulme Trustees for awarding a research grant to one of the authors for a study of the transition from subsistence to cash economies in underdeveloped countries. Much of the resulting information is given in Chapters III and IV.

[2] *National Museets Arbejdsmark*, 1953, p. 43.

[3] Galletti, Baldwin and Dina, *Nigerian Cocoa Farmers*, London, 1956.

[4] Private communication. See also W. H. Beckett, *Akosoaso*, London School of Economics Monograph in Social Anthropology, No. 10.

flint axes, heavier still. There is a present-day professor of archae-ology who gives demonstrations, slow but sure, of cutting down a small tree with a shaped flint which he holds in his hand; he has not measured the labour which the first agriculturists would have put into clearing a hectare of land, but it must have been consider-able.

Shifting cultivation is the most primitive type of agriculture. It has been defined by Pelzer[1] as 'an economy of which the main characteristics are rotation of fields rather than crops; clearing by means of fire; absence of draught animals and of manuring; use of human labour only; employment of the dibble stick or hoe; short periods of soil occupancy alternating with long fallow periods'. But, as he points out, just as advanced agriculture does not depend upon the animal-drawn plough, primitive agriculture does not depend upon the hoe; a more fundamental distinction may be made in terms of land use. Shifting cultivators clear with axes and hand knives preferably virgin forest (leaving the stumps of large trees scattered over the area), burn the brushwood, and raise a crop generally for one, two or three years in succession, after which the land is rested for periods up to twenty years or more to allow time for soil fertility to be restored by recovery of the natural vegetation.

This system of 'cut and burn', or shifting agriculture, has been not merely (as it had to be) the practice of pioneer agriculturists anywhere in the world; it has persisted over very long periods of time as the regular system of agriculture for most of the inhabitants of 'Black Africa' (i.e. from the Sahara down to the South African border), for many inhabitants of Latin America, and in some less densely populated regions in Asia.

In spite of the high initial input, overall labour requirements of shifting agriculture are low and discontinuous and, so long as land is available, the shifting cultivator finds this technique of produc-tion, per ton of grain produced, less laborious than those required in sedentary agriculture. Geddes[2] points out that in the mixed economy of the Land Dayak, in which both shifting and sedentary agriculture were practised for the production of rice, absolute yield per hectare is less important to the farmer than yield per unit of labour. Although all areas of sedentary swamp rice cultivation gave higher yields per ha., preference was invariably given to the pro-

[1] K. J. Pelzer, *Pioneer Settlement in the Asiatic Tropics*, New York, 1954.
[2] W. R. Geddes, *The Land Dayaks of Sarawak*. Colonial Research Study No. 14, H.M.S.O., 1954.

duction of rice in the hills cleared by 'cut and burn' methods. In his sample, yield per ha. was 1903 kg. paddy on the swamp, and only 1578 kg. paddy in the hills, but yield per man-hour worked was 0·87 kg. and 0·95 kg. respectively, with a total input of 2165 hours/ha. on the swamp and 1663 hours in the hills. This awareness of labour costs has been noted elsewhere in Borneo — a country in which there is a labour shortage. In Indonesia, however, with its heavy concentrations of population, the situation appears to be reversed. Leach[1] in North Borneo gives a yield of 1910 kg. paddy/ha. under best conditions of shifting agriculture, Izikowitz[2] 1150 kg. among the hill Lamet of Indo-China, and Freeman[3] 730 kg. among the pre-literate Iban of the hinterland of Sarawak. Statistics of grain yields obtained by primitive cultivators are, however, of little value except where data on kg. per man-hour worked are also available. Also, we do not know what access they have to other sources of food supply.

The fertility of the soil, it is said, is restored by the practice of abandoning clearings after a few years and resting the land for long periods. The word 'fertility' here is very ambiguous; and the questions of plant chemistry and soil science involved should be set out in a little more detail. Those familiar with the subject must excuse an elementary exposition.

The growth of a plant, besides its obvious requirements of air, sunlight and water, calls also for certain substances in the soil, to be taken in through its roots. Of the whole known range of elements, plants seem to require a great number, including such unlikely elements as zinc, manganese and boron, though only in minute traces. There is a great deal of further research still to be done in this field. Some areas of land are poor infertile heathlands because of deficiencies of certain trace elements; but this is not the question at issue for the shifting cultivator, who is no worse placed than many modern farmers in his inability to remedy such deficiencies.

Apart from trace elements, the plant finds absolutely necessary for growth, and has to draw from the soil by its roots in substantial quantities, nitrogen, phosphorus, potassium, calcium, sulphur, magnesium, and iron. The three latter appear to be present in adequate quantities in almost every soil. Of all the other four,

---

[1] E. R. Leach, 'Some Aspects of Dry Rice Cultivation in North Burma and British Borneo', *The Advancement of Science*, Vol. VI, No. 21, 1949, p. 28.

[2] K. G. Izikowitz, *Lamet: Hill Peasants in French Indo-China*, 1951.

[3] J. D. Freeman, *Iban Agriculture*. Colonial Office Research Study No. 18, 1955.

natural supplies are supplemented by modern farmers with their fertilizers.

But does not the soil also require to be adequately supplied with 'organic matter' or 'humus'? These two terms are somewhat indefinite, and in addition, unfortunately, have come to have emotional values attached to them. It is necessary therefore to describe the situation precisely. The literal meaning of the word 'organic', in this sense, is a compound containing the element carbon (generally excluding, however, the inorganic carbonates, and one or two other compounds). On this definition, certain artificial fertilizers, such as cyanamide and urea are 'organic' because they contain carbon, while others such as sulphate of ammonia are not. (This distinction may appear far-fetched, but it is already of importance in India, where urea is favoured as a more 'natural' fertilizer.) In communities lacking artificial fertilizers (including the whole world until a hundred years ago and, by definition, all shifting cultivators now), fertilization of the soil with additional supplies of nitrogen, phosphorus and potash can only be done through 'organic' means, i.e. manuring with the residues of plants and animals (though most of the calcium required for manuring soil was obtained from inorganic sources). This fact alone may account for the great and sometimes excessive concern for organic manures which many people feel.

The excreta of livestock make a most valuable form of manure available for people who cannot buy chemical fertilizers, since they concentrate in a limited area nitrogen, phosphorus and potash which may have been obtained by grazing over a wide area. The ashes of a tree have lost all their nitrogen in the process of burning, but yield considerable supplies of calcium, phosphorus and potash, particularly the latter, in much greater abundance than could be obtained in any other manner, because the deep roots of the trees bring back from the subsoil much of what had been leached (i.e. washed downwards by the action of water) from the top soil. Leaching is particularly rapid in high rainfall tropical areas, and so the top soil tends quickly to lose fertility which (for a cultivator who cannot buy artificial fertilizers, or keep livestock) can only be restored by periodically cutting and burning the trees.

'Humus' is a somewhat indefinite term for that part of the soil formed from decomposing plant and animal remains. The litter of fallen leaves, bark, etc., from a forest is an important source of humus. Its chemical structure is indefinite, including a great variety of organic compounds; it is also a very important source of nitrogen. There is still a great deal which is not known about the chemistry of nitrogen in soils, particularly in tropical soils; the amount of nitrogen available for plant growth fluctuates in a remarkable manner. It has long been known that certain leguminous plants will bring down nitrogen from the atmosphere to enrich the soil; but it has only recently been discovered that certain blue-green algae, found in a great variety of soils, also have the same capacity.

But humus must not be regarded solely as a source of nitrogen, which might eventually be replaced by artificial fertilizers, or cultivating algae, or some other device. The other organic compounds in the humus appear to be very important not so much for the chemistry as for the physics of the soil, helping it to preserve its 'crumb structure', by methods only partially understood. This 'structure' of the soil enables it to hold more water, which is very important in hot climates; and without it also a large part of the valuable top soil is liable to be eroded away by wind or rain. In any case, an abundant supply of organic matter in the soil probably helps the beneficial algae.

Most fertilizing just consists of reconcentrating, in the cultivated field, those chemical elements which had been scattered, in the grassland or the subsoil. Artificial fertilizing with potash or phosphorus draws upon the resources of certain mines in other parts of the world, whose supply, however, is limited. The artificial nitrogen fertilizers, on the other hand, draw on the nitrogen from the atmosphere, and there is no limit to their supply.

The burning of the fallen scrub by the shifting cultivator destroys the humus in the uppermost layers of the soil. Lower in the soil, the humus remains, and is the principal source — and probably not an adequate one — of nitrogen for the subsequent crop. As population increases, the shifting cultivator has to work on a rather shorter cycle of cutting and burning. The soil research work now in progress indicates that repeated burning at fairly short intervals, with the consequent destruction of humus, may have a very serious effect on the soil, leading eventually to a regrowth, in place of the previous thick scrub, of a thin savannah-type woodland, which when cleared yields a very infertile soil for cropping.

The burning however also completely destroys all weeds and weed seeds over the whole area. This constitutes one of its principal attractions for the tropical cultivator. For the first year at any rate, not only is the soil rich in phosphorus and potash (if not in nitrogen) but it is also weed-free. Weeds grow very fast in the tropics, and the difficulty of getting the weeding done during the growing season is the principal limiting factor on the amount of ground which a family can cultivate. In subsequent years, productivity rapidly falls off, and weed infestation becomes unmanageable, till the land has to be abandoned.

De la Pena, one of the leading officials of the Mexican Department of Agriculture, estimated[1] that as much as three million hectares in Mexico were still cultivated by 'shifting' methods, on a ten-year cycle on the average, and yielding $1\frac{1}{2}$ tons maize/ha. — a considerably better yield than that obtained by many sedentary cultivators. However, certain primitive maize cultivators, namely the North American Indians[2] of the seventeenth century, who had probably only acquired the art of maize growing a few centuries earlier, from further south — but who could practise rotational cultivation on fertile forest soils hitherto uncultivated — obtained yields of $2\frac{1}{2}$ tons/ha.

In Yucatan, the tropical southern part of Mexico, in the village of Chankom, Redfield and Villa[3] found that second-year yields were 25–50 per cent below first-year. The village had a population of 251 on 24·5 sq. km. of land, or just over 10 persons/sq. km. About half the land, however, appeared to be left permanently uncultivated, and the remainder cultivated on a nine-year cycle (two years cultivation and seven years fallow). The land cultivated in any one year is only 120 ha., or about 1·2 ha./cultivator. Yield of maize averages 1 ton/ha., or 480 kg. per head of the population of the village, of which 215 kg. is consumed, and the rest is available for sale. This shifting agriculture however appears to be socially unstable. The village of Chankom, established only fifty years previously, was already showing signs of disintegration — people were tending to leave the village, and to clear and cultivate individual plots for themselves in the more distant forest which might be more fertile.

The primitive pagan North Mamprusi people in Ghana were (at the time of Lynn's survey[4]) purely subsistence cultivators, growing no cash crop, and paying no taxes. Their recorded grain output

[1] World Population Conference, 1954, Rome.
[2] M. K. Bennett, *Journal of Political Economy*, October 1955.
[3] P. Gourou, *The Tropical World*, 3rd edition, 1961.
[4] C. W. Lynn, *Agriculture in North Mamprusi*. Gold Coast Department of Agriculture Bulletin No. 34, 1937.

was generally inadequate for their calorie requirements. They eked out their grain supplies by supplementing them with food from wild sources in a bad year; in a good year grain was used lavishly for religious ceremonies, and no attempt was made to store against poor returns in the following year. The shifting cultivators in Viet Nam[1] obtain an average of 198 kg. of rough rice per head per year. This figure is also inadequate. They probably also, however, obtain some additional food from natural sources.

Peters[2] made a valuable study of the Lala shifting cultivators of Northern Rhodesia, growing finger millet. He found their customary level of consumption of grain to be 232 kg./person/year, which just about provides their calorie requirements — they seem to have little in the way of other edible crops, though they may obtain some animal and plant food from the forest. The average cycle of regeneration has been seventeen years. Attempts to recultivate with a rotation of only 9 to 12 years, but otherwise using the same methods, yielded only 169 kg. grain/person/year. Families lacking the right to a share of the forest land, and thereby compelled to cultivate permanent plots, obtained a yield of only 208 kg./person/year. Some of the men from such families will have to go to seek wage work elsewhere. Peters also surveyed the information for the neighbouring tribes, and found a requirement of 250 kg. grain/person/year prevailed with considerable consistency.

Of the whole of south-east Asia below India and China, Dobby[3] has estimated that as much as a third is still cultivated by shifting cultivators. Conklin[4] studied the pygmy Hanunóo in the Philippines, whom he found to have a much more sophisticated system of shifting cultivation than the majority of the Africans, growing 280 specific food crop types of which several dozen are regularly cropped together with rice, and thus avoiding the dearth in the preharvest months which so many Africans suffer. The average cycle for a *swidden* (this is not a Filipino word, but an old English dialect word meaning 'burned clearing') lasted 12 years, of which 2–4 were cultivated, the remainder fallow. New swiddens are generally cut in second growth forest areas, the site of many previous plantings. Rice, the most valued crop, is planted for the first year

[1] K. G. Izikowitz, *Lamet: Hill Peasants in French Indo-China*, 1951.

[2] D. U. Peters, *Land Usage in Serenje District*, Rhodes-Livingstone Paper No. 19, 1950.

[3] E. H. G. Dobby, *South East Asia*, London, 1950.

[4] H. C. Conklin, *Hanunóo Agriculture*, a report on an integral system of shifting cultivation in the Philippines. FAO Forestry Development Paper No. 12, Rome, 1957.

on newly cleared swiddens. It is followed by other grain and root crops, whose growth appears to be compatible with the gradually renewed forest.

In Conklin's study, good information is given about labour inputs. Yields of rice are fairly high, averaging 2·3 tons rough rice/ha., with a range from 1·05 to 3·8, followed by a maize crop in the same year. Some 10–15 per cent of the agricultural product is traded, some of it for other foods, some for manufactures, including salt, beans, pottery, medicine, scented hair-oil, and flash lamps.

One of the most thorough studies of shifting cultivation has

TABLE VI. MAN-HOUR COSTS IN HANUNÓO SWIDDEN FARMING

(estimated annual minimum average labour requirement)
Based on available case data

		Man-Hours/ha. of New Swidden in		
		climax forest	second growth woody	bamboo
Stage	Activity			
1	Site selecting	6*	3*	3*
2	Slashing	60	100*	150
3	Felling*	350*	150	40
4	Firebreaking	10	40*	40*
	Firing	4*	2*	2*
	Reburning*	175	100*	50*
5	Planting maize	10	10	10
	Planting rice	150	130	130
	Interplanting	300	300	300
	Replanting	5	5	5
	Fencing	150	150	150
	Protecting	150*	75*	75*
	Guarding	400*	200*	200*
	1st weeding	}100	150	150
	2nd weeding		200	200
	Thinning and last weeding	200	250	250
6	Harvesting maize	80	80	80
	Harvesting rice	300	300	300
	Storing rice	30	30	30
	Cleaning	200	200	200*
7–8	Non-grain cultivation and harvesting	500*	500*	500*
	Total man-hours	3,180*	2,975*	2,865*

* closely related tasks included.

D

been made among the Iban in Sarawak.[1] Freeman quotes some
Malayan data showing that the first crop of rice on newly cleared
jungle land may be over 2 tons (rough weight)/ha.; but the second
crop about 1·5, the third crop below 1 ton/ha. The Iban however
obtained an average of only 0·73 tons — but the year of investigation was admittedly a poor one. The average area cultivated per
person was only 0·32 ha. Consumption of rice (rough weight) was
220 kg./person/year (i.e. some two-thirds of their total calorie
requirements); another 15 kg./person/year of rice were used for
seed, and 50 kg. used to feed poultry and hunting dogs, for
religious sacrifices, and for brewing beer. The cultivable land
available averaged 11 ha./person (70 per cent of the total area).
The average worker worked for 508 hours a year.

'When working in virgin jungle it is usual for the Iban to cultivate
half or more of a farm for two years in succession, but with rare exceptions a proportion of new forest is felled each year. In secondary jungle,
on the other hand, it is normal for the whole of the farmed area to be
abandoned after one crop has been taken.... When land is finally
allowed to revert to secondary growth, it is left for as long as possible,
and this is often for a period of 15 years or more.

A special feature of Iban agriculture is the cultivation of a wide range
of catch crops, interspersed on the same land as the padi (rice). A few,
such as ensabi (a kind of mustard plant, the leaves of which are eaten)
are sown separately, immediately after the burn. Others are planted
simultaneously with the padi, the seeds being mixed up in the same sow-
ing basket and sown into the same dibble holes. The most important of
these are cucumber, pumpkin, luffa, and gourd. All of these are ready to
eat before the padi has ripened.... Cucumber and pumpkin leaves are
cooked as vegetables as soon as they have formed.... Around the edges
of the farm clearing, and in the immediate vicinity of the hut (farm hut
or watch-house), which stands at its centre, various other plants are
grown, such as cassava, maize and pineapples....

Each season, some families succeed in producing a surplus, while
others find themselves with a deficit; and so, year by year, scores of
different families exchange gongs for padi or padi for gongs.... Brass
gongs are the principal form of property in which the Iban invest their
savings. These gongs have the great advantage of being untouched by
the Borneo climate and are virtually indestructible; further, they have a
marked prestige value and can be displayed and used on ceremonial
occasions.... It frequently happens however that a family is not prepared to part with any of its gongs or other property. In these circumstances recourse is had to the traditional scarcity food of the Iban —
sago. Most Bilek families possess small plantations of sago palms,
specially planted as a scarcity crop, for no Iban relishes *mulong* (as pre-

[1] J. D. Freeman, *Iban Agriculture*, Colonial Office Research Study No. 18,
1955.

pared sago is called), and it is only eaten under duress when padi cannot easily be procured. When planted sago is not available, the men set off to scour the jungle for the wild palms, from which the nomadic tribes of Borneo — such as the Punans — habitually obtain the sago which is the main item of their diet.'

Freeman's study is also valuable in giving us a detailed account of labour requirements for cultivating both virgin jungle and secondary jungle. Based on their average day worked of 6·6 hours, we have the following:

TABLE VII. TIME EXPENDED BY THE IBAN IN MAN-HOURS PER HECTARE

	Kampong (or virgin jungle)	Danum (or secondary jungle)
Slashing	98	82–98
Felling	195–228	65–82
Secondary clearing	32–82	32–82
Dibbling	65	65
Sowing	82	82
Weeding	195–260	244–326
Reaping	228–326	228–326
Transporting	17	17
Minimum total	913	815
Maximum total	1158	1076

Cultivation appears to have been much less intensive than among the Hanunóo. Figures do not include however certain kinds of work such as constructing fences, erecting traps, and the crucially important job of standing guard over the ripening paddy. Weeding, here as in Africa, is seen to be a limiting factor. The time within which it has to be completed is short, if the crop is not to be spoiled; and the work is considered too degrading for men to do, although sometimes the older men will help if the amount of land to be weeded exceeds 0·8 ha./woman available.

If a family do not have sufficient labour to complete their harvesting, they will hire a neighbour, paying him a gantang (2·4 kg.) of rough rice/day together with a mid-day meal or, in effect, the value of about 3 kg. rough rice/day. As will be seen later, this is the order of magnitude of the real wage which has prevailed among near-subsistence cultivators in different parts of the world, at different times.

Uganda now has about 0.5 ha./person of *cultivated* land. As population density has increased, the proportion of land that could be left to rest has naturally declined. In one small area in Teso which was subject to intensive agricultural surveys in 1937 and 1953 the ratio of resting to cropped land dropped between these two dates from 1·5 to 1·2. These figures may be typical of the densely populated districts. For the country as a whole, the annual reports of the Agricultural Department give a ratio of available to cultivated land of 7:0 in 1952 and 6:8 in 1960.

Lack of adequate female labour in the weeding season limits the amount of food which can be grown, and it may be that one of the best services which well-wishers could render to primitive cultivators is to supply them with herbicides, together with sufficient technical staff to supervise their application (if wrongly mixed, they may kill the crop as well as the weeds.) But anything which can persuade them that weeding is not necessarily degrading work for a man, and that the men should help the women at this task, will do much good. There are signs that the change is taking place. 'Within the peasant family itself there are signs that the old distinction of work between the sexes is beginning to break down. In the Eastern Province of Uganda women can be found ploughing and men weeding.'[1]

The question is also raised whether we could not do a good service to African cultivators by redesigning their tools for them. But they have advanced a long way from the simple wooden digging sticks which were used by their remote ancestors (and by ours: and which can still be seen in some of the most isolated regions of New Guinea). Some Africans had discovered how to work iron before their contacts with Europe began in the fifteenth century. Iron has always been an expensive commodity for primitive peoples, and they use it as sparingly as they can. Nevertheless, they have discovered how to make large-bladed hoes, which can move as much earth as the large iron spade of the European gardener. Separate hoes have been designed for men and for women, carefully adapted to their strength and stature. Many of those familiar with the problem believe that African empiricism has already discovered as much as any European designer could when faced with this problem, although Allard[2] concluded that redesigned hoes for hand weeding could give a productivity 10–20 per cent higher than traditional hoes.

[1] G. B. Masefield, *Agricultural Change in Uganda*, Food Research Institute Studies, Vol. III, No. 2, 1962.
[2] *Bulletin Agricole du Congo Belge*, 1960, pp. 603–615.

TABLE VIII. NUMERICAL DATA ON SHIFTING CULTIVATORS

Name of tribe	Country	Date	Ha./person/year Felled	Ha./person/year Cultivated	Production in grain equivalents kg/person/year	Average persons/family	Percentage of family available for agricultural work	Average hours/year worked	Principal crop
Iban	Sarawak	1949–51	0·32	0·24	176[a]	5·7	60	508[b]	Hill rice
Land Dayaks	Sarawak	1949–51		0·28	219[a]	7·0	60[c]	640[d]	Hill and swamp rice
Dusun	Borneo			1·52[f]	319–525[h]	4·2	60[g]	588[d]	Rice and rubber[e]
Lala, Serenje Plateau	N. Rhodesia	1944–5							Finger millet
Cycle over 20 years			0·097	0·069	298	4·5			do.
Cycle 17–20 years			0·105	0·073	250	5·9			do.
Cycle 13–16 years			0·069[i]	0·049	265	7·5			do.
Cycle 9–12 years			0·057[i]	0·036	169	6·1			do.
North Mamprusi	Ghana	1932–6		0·27	171	12·0		548	Millet and sorghum

[a] Rough rice.
[b] 77 days of 6·6 hours.
[c] Assumed 6·6 hours/day.
[d] Assumed.
[e] Described as 'in a state of transition from primitive culture'. Rubber converted at 2:1 kg. rough rice (ratio prevailing before the 1950 boom). Draught animals are used to the extent of 25 buffalo days/ha. cultivated.

Assumed. Precise figure cannot be ascertained as the villagers prefer to exchange labour with each other and to work in groups.

[f] Of which 1·20 under rubber (57 per cent of all families had rubber plantations).
[g] Assumed.
[h] For rice and rubber respectively.
[i] Cultivators who clear the forest on a long rotation leave the large trees standing. On a short rotation they clear the scrub more thoroughly, and hence are only able to undertake a smaller area.

We may now consider the densities of population which are possible with primitive shifting agriculture. The reader must beware of becoming confused between the sq. km./person, which are the units in which we measured population densities for hunting people, and the persons/sq. km. which we are using now.

We should remind ourselves that the primitive pastoral communities, found where the land is not forested, and may indeed be semi-arid, live at a density of about 2 persons/sq. km.[1] Though not so wasteful of the land and its resources as are the primitive hunting peoples, they nevertheless fall far short of fully exploiting the potential mean output of the land, which Pirie estimates at 50 kg. liveweight gain/ha./year (5 tons liveweight gain/sq. km.). Even if we halve this figure, as some would do, it seems clear that primitive pastoral peoples, lacking fences, haymaking implements, etc., are unable to exploit the full growth of grass in the favourable seasons of the year; and also they probably lose many livestock to predatory animals.

In the highly productive agriculture of the Hanunóo, a cycle of 12 years is required, and about 20 per cent of the land is deemed uncultivable for 'ritual, geographical or vegetational reasons'. Nevertheless, Conklin computes the maximum population capacity of the land at as high as 39 persons/sq. km. Van Beukering[2] reached very similar conclusions about maximum possible population density in studying primitive peoples in Indonesia with a culture similar to that of the Hanunóo.

On the other hand, for the Iban in Sarawak, Freeman calculated that there was a danger of land degradation when the ratio rose above 20 persons/sq. km.; he drew his own sample in the Baleh region, where the figure stood at 5–6 only.

Gourou[3] also quotes a great range of figures, from 10 persons/sq. km. as the maximum satisfactory density for the primitive growers of upland (i.e. unirrigated) rice in the Ivory Coast of West Africa, to 120 for the Sacatepequez province of Guatemala. This is the only malaria-free province in Guatemala, which helps to explain the high density. Owners of coffee plantations in this province, at any rate until recently, persuaded the Guatemalan government to

[1] Rätzel, quoted by Taylor, *Canadian Journal of Economics and Political Science*, August 1950.
[2] J. A. van Beukering, *Het Ladagvraagstuk, een Bedrijfs — en sociaal economisch probleem*, Mededeelingen van het Department van Economische Zaken in Nederlandsch-Indie, No. 9, 1947.
[3] P. Gourou, *The Tropical World*, 3rd edition, 1961.

impose forced labour to enable them to obtain their labour requirements; this at any rate is a good indication that there was among
the subsistence cultivators no serious underoccupation below the
level of employment to which they were accustomed. In some
regions in Sumatra, Gourou found maximum population densities
ranging from 15 to 40 persons/sq. km., with a seven-year cycle of
cultivation, and with about half the land too rough or too swampy
to be cultivated at all.

Studies of the Lala, shifting cultivators of the dry Serenje
plateau in Northern Rhodesia, by Peters,[1] indicated, however,
that deterioration of the natural resources of the land might occur
when population density rose no higher than 2 persons/sq. km. In
1945 he found the land in an advanced stage of degradation, though
the mean density of population over the whole plateau was only
3 persons/sq. km. As a result of this, they were in a process of
transition to a more settled type of agriculture, with subsidiary but
permanent hoed gardens which did not share in the degenerative
process of 'cut and burn' agriculture; the gardens were maintained
in one spot as long as the village remained in existence. Sedentary
or permanent cultivation in which peasant cultivators till the same
piece of land year after year, in combination with irrigation on
flooded plains or in delta regions, will support considerably higher
population densities. Employing buffaloes for the heavy labour of
ploughing and carrying home the grain, the Dusun, settled cultivators of the Penampang plains in North Borneo,[2] obtain an
average of 325 kg. of paddy/head/year from the cultivation of wet
rice, which compares closely with the estimated minimum requirement. Combining the output of rice and rubber, the economic
grain equivalent produced averaged 537 kg./head/year. Perhaps
more important to the peasant than the labour of draught animals
in terms of crop yields is the manure applied to his fields. In Glyn-
Jones's sample, a small amount of grazing was available; in
addition, they graze rice fields which are thus manured. No
systematic feeding of livestock is practised.

One of the writers has been able to observe a later stage of the
process among the Mandingo tribe in Gambia. In 1950, the shifting
cultivation of plateau lands was supplemented by rice grown continuously on annually flooded river flats. It was estimated that these

[1] D. U. Peters, *Land Usage in Serenje District*, Rhodes-Livingstone Paper
No. 19, 1950.
[2] M. Glyn-Jones, *The Dusun of the Penampang Plains in North Borneo*, Report
to the Colonial Office (unpublished).

plateau lands had all been cleared over periods ranging from 15 to 50 years. The more favoured sandy loams fringing the river valley were no longer cropped under shifting cultivation, but were cultivated continuously. 'Cut and burn' cultivations further afield, under these conditions of population pressure, were sometimes cultivated for three or five years continuously, as against the three which seem to be the safe maximum for 'cut and burn' cultivators; in such cases (growing millet) the crops of the later years were often total failures. Twelve years after, in 1962, it was found that breakdown of the extended family to form nuclear family units had left most households short of men to work at shifting cultivation, men being willing to join the women in the more intensive cultivation of rice swamp lands in the river valley.

While interesting examples of an economy in transition from shifting to settled agriculture can be found, a great deal of Africa still subsists by shifting cultivation.[1] Gourou[2] estimates that in the whole of 'Black Africa' (Africa excluding the Sahara and north thereof, and the Republic of South Africa) the amount of land cultivated, in any one year, is about one-thirtieth of the potential cultivable land. It is not that Africans are ignorant of, or incapable of, settled intensive agriculture. The island of Ukara in Lake Victoria (Tanganyika) maintains an agricultural population at a density of 225 persons/sq. km.; or an even higher density if we take into account the hills of bare rock, which constitute a large part of the area of the island. On this island is found some of the most intensive agriculture in the world, with every field cropped twice a year, cattle fed on cultivated fodder crops and kept in sheds, and the manure carefully spread. Similar though less striking examples of intensive agriculture are found in a few other isolated parts of Africa, including the mountains of Madagascar. It appears that there are historical reasons for these settlements, where the people have been hemmed in by enemies, and compelled to subsist on much smaller areas than they would like. The system of shifting cultivation must be judged to be a definite preference on the African's part. So long as abundant land is available, as it is in most

---

[1] In growing cereals on poor pasture land, so as to increase the yield, the African cuts the grass and heaps it into little piles, which are then burned. The whole field is then prepared and sown. At harvest time the treated areas bear vigorous clumps of grain, while the rest of the field has a poverty-stricken aspect. See P. P. Leurquin, *Agricultural Change in Ruanda-Usundi, 1945–60*, Stanford, Food Research Institute, 1963.

[2] P. Gourou, private communication.

of Africa, it yields him better returns, in kg. grain/man-hour of labour input, than does settled agriculture.

To Gourou, a man of fertile ideas, we owe another very interesting proposition[1] concerning the Maya civilization, which flourished in Central America about the sixth century A.D., in Yucatan, a hot humid area of dense forest growth. One geographer, with a preconception that civilizations can never flourish in such areas, has hypothecated that the climate in the sixth century must have been very different from what it is now. In support of this theory not a single fragment of direct evidence is available. From the large stone buildings which the Maya left, only recently uncovered from thick jungle, we must conclude that they had an advanced civilization, also some knowledge of astronomy and mathematics. From counts of the numbers of their houses it has been estimated that their population density averaged 60 persons/sq. km. Their agricultural methods, however, were the same 'cut and burn' method of maize cultivation which is used by their successors in the same area to-day. Gourou points out that so dense a population, using these methods, must inevitably have been confronted before long by exhaustion of soil fertility; and the population which supported the cities and temples must have been compelled to scatter again. In this factor alone he can see the cause of the disappearance of the Maya civilization.

The Inca and Aztec civilizations also depended upon maize grown by similar methods. The Inca, however, lived in a low rainfall area where the soil does not lose fertility so rapidly through leaching, and irrigated their crops, thereby probably obtaining high yields. The Aztecs inhabited country of intermediate climatic type. It is interesting to notice however that they built their capital city on a lake, thereby making possible for themselves a system of transport tapping a more extensive area than was possible for the Maya with their loads carried on men's heads along jungle paths.

[1] P. Gourou, *The Tropical World*, 3rd edition, 1961.

CHAPTER IV

Agricultural Progress Measured in Grain Equivalents

The wheat which supplies our bread undergoes various milling processes, removing the outer layers of the grain, which are sold for animal feeding, until (except for the minority who like wholemeal bread) only about two-thirds of the weight of the original grain is left. The demand, on the part of most consumers, for highly milled white flour is a matter of taste and choice; the fact that people can consume 'wholemeal' bread indicates that such a high degree of milling is not a physiological necessity. But on the other hand, it appears that we are not entitled to say that the whole wheat grain (after crushing and cooking, but without milling away any of the bran, etc.) is edible and digestible by human beings, as it is by animals. There appears to be some difference of medical opinion on this point. 'Bran is used industrially for polishing steel', said one medical upholder of the view against eating it, 'but why use it on your intestines?'

The same conclusion is upheld when we examine the information obtained by those who study African life, in various parts of the continent. African tribesmen's knowledge of medicine is very limited; but they are often short of food, and have to economize their supplies carefully, and not allow any avoidable waste. The consensus of opinion among those who have examined this matter appears to be that Africans, even when threatened by hunger, still consider it necessary to mill off something like 10 per cent of the wheat or other grain which they may be consuming. Long experience may have taught them that this portion of the grain is indigestible by the human interior, even for a hungry man.

Further medical study is necessary before this question is settled. But for the present, to be safe, we will assume that it is necessary[1] to mill off 10 per cent by weight of any wheat, maize, millet,

---

[1] Platt however implies only 2 per cent inedible. See *Tables of Representative Values of Food Commonly Used in Tropical Countries*, Medical Research Council Special Report No. 302, 1962.

sorghum, etc., consumed. The millings, of course, are available to feed livestock.

In the case of rice, the problem is different. The husk is clearly inedible by humans. Its removal leaves 'brown rice', weighing about 80 per cent of the original rough rice. But even the most austere consumers find a certain amount of further milling necessary. The milled rice eaten in Japan is $73\frac{1}{2}$ per cent of the original weight, and an even higher figure appears to prevail in Formosa. Most rice-eating countries, on the other hand, mill the grain down further to a weight averaging some 67 per cent of the original rough rice, as low as 60 per cent in some cases.

A kg. of wheat or similar grain, therefore, in the hands of a cultivator who has to exercise strict economy, will be milled down to 900 g., which will yield 3150 calories. The table in Chapter I showed that calorie requirements per day, averaged over the whole population, men, women and children, might be as low as 1985 for the smallest bodied people, in the warmest climate, with the men averaging only 4 hours' work per day, to 2365 for a larger-bodied people, in a colder climate, with the men working 8 hours per day.

It follows that a community living entirely on grain (with a few wild plants, or other source to supply vitamins and minerals) will require, at this rate, anything from 630 to 750 g./person/day, according to the varying circumstances described above, or 230 to 274 kg./person/year of *unmilled* grain. These figures might be reduced a little for people consuming the grains (certain millets) which have higher calorie values than other grains, but only by about 5 per cent.

The protein content of grain is very variable, but it averages over 11 per cent. People consuming grain at this rate therefore, would obtain sufficient protein, even on the higher scales formerly thought necessary; certainly on Waterlow's scale of only 35 g./person/day.

Some 250 kg. of grain/person/year can therefore be called the subsistence minimum.

But this is still rather an abstract figure. Even the poorest community will want some break in the endless monotony of a cereal diet, something which adds flavour without being always the most economical source of calories and proteins, some meat or fish or fruit, which may make a call upon agricultural resources which would otherwise be devoted to growing cereals. Moreover, in most parts of the world, clothes are necessary for warmth as well as for decency. Poor agricultural communities now no longer have the abundant supply of animal skins which were available to their ancestors in hunting communities, and they cannot afford to buy artificial fibres, so they must devote some of their agricultural resources to producing cotton, flax, or other fibre to make their clothes. Studies by FAO show that even the poorest communities require about 1·5 kg./person/year of fibre.

Is there any convenient way of relating these requirements of fibre, and of other non-cereal products which poor communities may produce in small quantities, to their main crop of cereals?

It is clear that the conversion of other products on calories alone, as is sometimes proposed, would not be satisfactory. Were we to do this, we should have to reckon a ton of meat as approximately equivalent to a ton of grain — whereas we know that the meat contains valuable proteins, and that almost everywhere in the world it would be readily exchangeable for six or seven tons of grain. Furthermore, a calorie basis for comparison would mean that we would have to put no value at all upon numerous agricultural products which people are glad to have for various purposes — cotton, tobacco, jute, coffee, tea, and so on.

This issue was met for the first time, it appears, by Buck in his book, *Land Utilization in China*. In comparing productivity, income and so on between farms in an advanced country, we bring into account the different products, and the different costs, by expressing them all in money as a common unit. This procedure comes so naturally to us that it seems pedantic even to describe it. It appeared to Buck, quite rightly, that this was not the way to measure output in a subsistence agricultural community such as China. Even where we can put a price on a crop, which is by no means always the case, there are doubts as to how far it really represents its value under these circumstances. Most of the crop may be grown for subsistence consumption, and only a small and unrepresentative part of it traded for money. The natural unit for measuring production in such a community is the kg. of grain. Buck therefore took as his unit one kg. of whatever type of grain was predominantly consumed in the neighbourhood (measuring rice with the husks removed, other grains raw). Potatoes and similar root crops he valued at 15 per cent of the corresponding weight of grain — their relative calorie content is about 20 per cent, but as they contain very little protein, 15 per cent is quite a fair value. All other products were converted to grain equivalents in accordance with the rates at which they exchanged against grain (sometimes the exchanges were in fact actual barters of various commodities, rather than money transactions) in the local markets — not necessarily using the same exchange rates throughout China. Buck also converted oilseeds and légumes into grain equivalents on the basis of their calorie value. He omitted livestock products altogether; but as in any case these are produced in such small quantities in China, the omission did no serious harm.

To apply this method of reckoning to the productivity of farmers in America or western Europe, expressing all their output as tons of 'grain equivalents', would be pedantic and misleading. The critic will rightly point out that the results would vary very greatly according to the exchange ratios of other products against grain, which vary greatly between country and country, and indeed between year and year. But in a subsistence economy, by definition, the greater part of the output must in any case consist of grain (or root crops). The amount of other products is comparatively small; and uncertainties about their valuation will therefore affect the result much less. One significant difference between low-income and high-income agricultural communities is that the relative price of fruit and vegetables, expressed in terms of grain, is much lower in the low-income communities.

Converted into grain equivalents, the minimum allowance of $1\frac{1}{2}$ kg./person/year for textile fibres becomes 14 kg. We must also make some allowance, though we cannot put a precise figure to it, for other agricultural products besides grains and roots required, even under the most austere conditions. Our final conclusion is that subsistence requirements, expressed in our units of grain equivalents, are somewhere between 250 and 300 kg./person/year, varying substantially, as we have seen, with climate and average body weight.

It should be added that a community producing precisely the minimum requirements, calculated as above, unless their harvests year by year are strictly uniform, or unless they keep reserves, will be intermittently hungry in bad seasons.

Grain equivalents as a measuring device were also used very successfully by de Vries, at that time Agricultural Adviser to the International Bank in Washington.[1] De Vries expressed all output in Asian countries in terms of milled rice per head of total popula-

[1] Now Rector of the School of Social Studies, The Hague; previously he had worked for many years in Indonesia.

tion (not only of population engaged in agriculture). His method, and that used below, differ somewhat from Buck's, in that another grain, say millet, which has almost the same calorific value as milled rice, but which sells at a lower price in local markets, because it is much less palatable, is converted into rice equivalents in accordance with this price — unlike Buck's procedure, where all grains count equally.

De Vries classified production, measured in *milled* rice equivalents, in a number of Asian countries, as follows:

TABLE IX. ASIA'S AGRICULTURAL OUTPUT IN MILLED
RICE

Equivalents Kg./Head of Population

	1934–8	1951–2
Pakistan	387	367
India	300	260
Ceylon	490	438
Burma	561	369
Thailand	343	397
Indo-China (Viet Nam)	455	311
Formosa	650	374
Philippines	432	380
Indonesia	365	306
Malaya	919	1037

In Viet Nam in 1939,[1] where population densities are extraordinarily high, the more prosperous 40–50 per cent of the population, representing the families of those who own more than 1 ha. of land and more than one draught animal, had an average income of 1810 francs, equivalent to 2070 kg. milled rice/family/year; the remainder of the population just about half that. Even allowing for some supplementation of the rice by vegetables, fish, etc., it is clear that a considerable number must have been very close to true subsistence level.

It will be seen how great the variation is, even between Asian countries. The very low figure shown for India for 1951–2 was probably based on the current production statistics, which are now known to have been defective; even so, and even after adding substantial food imports which India was receiving at that time, the figure is uncomfortably close to the subsistence minimum. There was a substantial production for export of rice in Burma, and of rice and sugar in Formosa, even in 1951–2. Malaya, Ceylon and, to

[1] P. Gourou, Institute of Pacific Relations, Ninth Conference, 1945.

a lesser extent, Indonesia have been producers of rubber, tea and other specialized export crops, whose price is determined in the world market, where it fluctuates considerably — a temporary high price for rubber accounts for the high figure shown for Malaya in 1951–2.

It was from examining these and related data that de Vries ventured on a bold and extremely fruitful generalization about the stages of agricultural progress, all measurements being made in kg. of unmilled grain equivalent/total population/year. The true subsistence minimum stands a little below 300 kg. grain equivalent/person/year. As production increases, perhaps to a level of 350, most of the increased product, not unexpectedly, is used to improve the diet. Even under these circumstances however a certain proportion of the crop has to be set aside for the purchase of a few necessary non-food commodities, payment of taxes, etc.

By the time a production per head of 400 units has been reached, however, the community is selling a substantial part of its agricultural product — this indicates, in effect, the urgency of other needs besides food, for clothing, building materials, medicine, and so forth. In the very poorest subsistence communities practically every family has to work on the land, and anything which they have in the way of non-agricultural goods or services, i.e. minimum requirements of clothing, shelter, etc., has to be provided by their own part-time efforts. As production rises, it is possible to sell some of the agricultural output in exchange for imports from a distance, or to employ a certain number of full-time craftsmen.

Not until 500 units have been reached is it worth while employing animal rather than human labour. Up to 750 units, draught and meat animals alike have to live on straw, bran and other by-products, together with a little grazing (de Vries suggests that 600 units may be about the point at which communities find it possible to set aside some land for pasture) — and the animals do not thrive on it. Possibly a little grain is spared for the work animals at the busiest season of the year when they most need encouragement. It is only beyond the productivity figure of 750 units that there is enough grain to spare for regular feeding to livestock, particularly to pigs and poultry, who cannot digest cellulose as cattle do, but require concentrated food in the form of grain or roots, as do we. It is at this stage that the cultivator should decide that the feeding of grain to livestock is worth while. The characteristic economy of western European and North American agriculture has now begun.

An illustration of a case where cereals are abundant, and poultry can be kept, comes from Thailand. Janlekha[1] estimates that in the Minburi village area, a chicken of an average farm family helps itself to up to 40 kg. of rice (4 tangs of paddy) annually. The cost of raising chickens for the farmer is entirely in paddy. The average hen lays about 143 eggs a year or 36 eggs (say 1·5 kg.) for every tang (10 kg.) of paddy she eats. Most of the eggs are sold for approximately 4 baht per dozen, and since a tang of paddy costs about 7 baht the gross profit is nominally 70 per cent. This means a steady cosy little income for the Thai peasant, even if he has to spend it at once on other foods.

Economic grain equivalent in kg./bird/year can be computed as follows:

Production	67·21
Consumption (3·25 oz/bird/day)	39·92

We get a good illustration of de Vries's principle from Naylor's classification[2] of groups of farms in Iraq.

Kg. Grain Equivalent/Person/Year

Net farm product after meeting animal feeding, seed and irrigation charges	Cash sales of farm products	Grain fed to livestock (deducted before computing net income)
500	13	163
737	203	226
1089	446	424
1820	1042	327

A supply of grain for feeding animals of 163 kg./person/year would hardly enable a family of five to keep one small working horse, at any rate in a country where hay is scarce. At the higher income levels, on the other hand, in a country where the keeping of pigs is forbidden, and poultry are probably greatly subject to disease, grain supply to animals seems to level out at about 400 kg/person/year, leaving more to be sold for cash on the higher productivity farms.

Now that our agriculture has entered the tractor age, we tend to think of that as having been preceded by a 'horse age' of im-

---

[1] J. E. de Young, *Village Life in Modern Thailand*, 1955, p. 100.
[2] Privately communicated.

memorial antiquity. In fact, the horse cultivation of the nineteenth and early twentieth centuries represented an important technical advance on what had gone before. In many parts of Europe ox ploughs are still to be found; they were predominant in this country until the late eighteenth century, and survived into the nineteenth century in Scotland. In Yugoslavia, to take an interesting modern example, horse cultivation is only general in Voivodina, the wealthiest and most developed part of the country, and ox cultivation prevails elsewhere. It is true that the technique of ploughing with oxen was much the same for an eighteenth-century peasant in England, for an Asian at the present day, as described by Virgil in the Georgics, or even as used by Homer's contemporaries. But even the ox plough represents an important technical advance on the most basic form of agriculture, namely cultivating the soil by hand hoes. This primitive and laborious form of agriculture is still the practice of the majority of African cultivators, of a substantial number in Asia, and of many in Latin America.

There is an economic equilibrium between the ox plough and the hand hoe. De Vries[1] stated that, under current conditions in Indonesia, the cost of keeping a buffalo only doubtfully balanced the additional output obtained through his labours; and that there were, in fact, signs of the economy slipping back to hand cultivation. Two buffaloes with a plough will cultivate three times as fast as hand cultivation on a large plot, but only $1\frac{1}{2}$ times as fast on a small plot.[2] In those regions with a very short wet season, however (discussed below), it may be necessary for the cultivator to use draught animals, whatever the cost, in order to get his cultivation done in time.

A similar regression appears to have been taking place in the community of which the grandfather of one of the authors was a member, namely the Scottish highlands[3] in the early nineteenth century. Increasing population density, higher rents, and lower prices for their produce, meant that crofters in some of the poorer districts were unable to afford even ox ploughs, and reverted to hand cultivation. In the months January to April it was estimated that a man could dig 2 ha.

It is true that there is an important exception which proves the rule. Japan, although a technically advanced country in other

---

[1] E. de Vries, World Population Conference, Rome, 1954.
[2] van der Koppel, *Die Landbouw in den Indischen Archipel.*
[3] M. Gray, *The Highland Economy, 1750–1850*, Edinburgh, 1957.

directions, is still largely using hand cultivation. India, at a lower level of productivity, keeps milch cattle (though they yield very little milk) and uses ox ploughs, and apparently has been using them for a very long time. Maybe they descend from an age when productivity was higher, and cattle were easier to feed. Also perhaps without them the cultivation of the lands of central India, with their very short wet season, would probably not have been possible. But in any case, as the slaughter of cattle is forbidden in India, farmers prefer to use at any rate the stronger cattle as draught animals.

It is also true that, over large areas of Africa, the use of both cattle and horses has been prevented by the tsetse fly, which carries trypanosomiasis. It has been shown in some areas that this destructive pest can be eliminated though the problem still remains as to how to keep the fly out once this has been done. It does *not*, however, follow that draught animals will soon be introduced into these areas — the level of productivity is still too low in many cases.

An illustration of this was recently found in Gambia by one of the writers[1] in which an attempt had been made unsuccessfully to introduce draught oxen into a hand-hoe economy; the cultivators insisted that they could not feed both themselves and the oxen. Measurement of agricultural output in *milled* rice equivalents showed that the level of productivity did not exceed 438 kg./person/year, and averaged only 270 kg. The ration recommended for draught oxen included 1 kg. grain/beast/day. Though the local type of ox is a mixture of Ndama and Zebu breeds, with a noticeable predominance of Ndama blood which accounts for its relatively high degree of resistance to trypanosomiasis, there is grave risk of over-worked and under-fed draught oxen going down with this disease.

The use of draught animals leads to a further substantial increase in production, *if* sufficient land is available, as it is generally in Africa. In many regions in the Middle East and Asia, however, there is not sufficient land to keep all the cultivating families occupied if they use draught oxen; there ensues, therefore, 'disguised unemployment' until (and this may take a very long time) new labour-intensive types of farming can be introduced (silk,

[1] M. R. Haswell, *The changing patterns of economic activity in a Gambia village*, Department of Technical Co-operation Overseas Research Publications No. 2., 1963.

tobacco, fruit, etc.); or until more urban employment becomes available.

India reports some 0·4 cattle per head of total population, 0·1 sheep, a somewhat larger number of goats, and an insignificant number of pigs (which are regarded as unclean by most caste Indians). Buck's figures for China show only 0·17 draught animals/head of rural population, 0·16 pigs, 0·12 sheep and goats, 0·7 poultry, and an inappreciable number of dairy cows.

Gilbert Slater[1] pioneered detailed surveys of some southern Indian villages in 1916, and the University of Madras resurveyed the same villages in 1936–7. Agricultural production per head had fallen over this period, and with it the number of livestock carried.

Name of Village:	Vadamalaipuram		Guruvayur	
Grain used as basis for 'grain equivalents':	Millet		Paddy	
	1916–17	1936–7	1916–17	1936–7
Kg. grain equivalent/ person/year		394	398	304
Livestock/person				
Cattle and buffaloes	0·60	0·61	0·42	0·18
of which milk animals	0·14	0·07	0·06	0·03
Sheep and goats	1·71	0·72	0·15	0·05
Pigs	0·06	—	a	a
Poultry	—	0·62	—	—
Kg. milk/milking animal				
Cows				345
Buffaloes				487
Kg. milk/person				
Cows				4·1
Buffaloes				6·8

a Included with sheep and goats.

Buck's device of converting all agricultural products to a common unit by using prices prevailing in local markets has much to commend it, especially when dealing with information from Chinese villages and other remote places. These advantages, however, appear to be overshadowed by the advantages of having a uniform scale for all countries, if we wish to make international comparisons. Furthermore, it is desirable to choose a scale which will accord with the weighting system now used by FAO for the construction of their

[1] G. Slater (editor), *Some South Indian Villages*, University of Madras, Economic Series 1, 1918.

index numbers of agricultural production, which are based upon regional wheat relative price weights for different parts of the world. For the purposes of this book, a median has been taken of the three FAO regions — the Near East, the Far East, and Africa.

FAO weights for cattle, pigs, sheep and poultry have been converted to meat on the basis of available information on slaughter rates, average carcase weights, and meat production under tropical conditions. Cattle for beef are killed older and leaner than in temperate climates, when the meat is said to have more flavour. Sheep are less well finished, and have less wool, in the tropics; pigs are smaller and are apt to mature at lighter weights.

Apart from grains referred to above, conversion coefficients for one or two principal crops may be noted: the shelled equivalent of unshelled groundnuts does not vary unduly, averaging about 67 per cent. The ginned yield of unginned cotton may range from 25 to 33 per cent, however, whilst the conversion coefficient for wool is much higher in the tropics than in Britain where fleeces are rain washed; the average clean yield of greasy wool is 67 per cent in Britain compared with 52–56 per cent in the tropics.

As has already been stated, even the poorest subsistence community finds wheat bran indigestible, at any rate in large quantities, and so they mill off about 10 per cent of the weight of wheat, being left with a residue which yields about 3·4 calories/g., or 3·06 calories/g. raw wheat (if they had eaten the wheat unmilled they might have obtained, according to the reference books, 3·16 calories/g.).

Now that we have before us food consumption data in a number of countries which can be restated in wheat equivalents, we can test our theory about the nature of diets. The poorest communities, we have estimated, will probably make their diets as economical as possible or, in other words, will aim at getting near to three calories for every g. of wheat equivalent consumed. (Theoretically, they might do even better; if they lived entirely on millet, sorghum or buckwheat, which most people find unpalatable, they would be getting as many calories from each g. as they do from a g. of wheat, while only having consumed two-thirds of a g. of 'wheat equivalent', according to the measures which we are now using.)

This theory is seen to be approximately borne out. Even the poorest community, however, cannot get higher than 2·85 calories per g. of economic wheat equivalent consumed. At higher levels of consumption, this ratio falls off rapidly, as an increasing proportion of fruit, meat, dairy products, etc., palatable but costly in terms of wheat equivalent, are included in the diet.

TABLE X. ECONOMIC AND CALORIE VALUE OF DIETS

Country	Food consumption expressed in kg. economic wheat equivalent per person per year	Calories Per capita per day (actual)	Per gramme of economic wheat equivalent consumed
Former Fr. West Africa (excluding Guinea)	314	2450	2·85
Angola	330	2215	2·45
Tanganyika	334	2175	2·38
Guinea	335	2400	2·61
Liberia	341	2540	2·72
Togo	344	2645	2·81
Former Fr. Equatorial Africa	354	2575	2·66
India	354	2050	2·11
Congo and Ruanda Urundi	363	2650	2·66
Kenya	366	2240	2·23
Haiti	377	1875	1·81
Guatemala	379	2175	2·09
Pakistan	383	2030	1·93
Honduras	389	2190	2·05
Cameroun	397	2470	2·27
Libya	398	2180	2·00
El Salvador	400	1975	1·80
Fed. of Rhodesia and Nyasaland	416	2500	2·19
Nigeria and the British Cameroons	435	2680	2·25
Ecuador	444	1935	1·59
South Korea	448	2040	1·66
Ethiopia	464	2295	1·81
Indonesia	471	2125	1·65
Ghana	477	2605	1·99
Egypt	480	2340	1·78
Dominican Republic	480	1950	1·48
Burma	485	2150	1·62
Syria	491	2225	1·65
Bolivia	492	1880	1·39
Tunisia	502	2170	1·58
Ceylon	514	2060	1·46

Country	Food consumption expressed in kg. economic wheat equivalent per person per year	Per capita per day (actual)	Calories Per Gramme of economic wheat equivalent consumed
Thailand	518	2185	1·54
Peru	527	2040	1·41
Malaya	528	2290	1·58
Iraq	536	2255	1·54
Iran	537	2040	1·38
Japan	549	2310	1·54
Taiwan	551	2430	1·55
Lebanon	553	2415	1·59
Morocco	556	2480	1·63
Sudan	561	2295	1·49
Mexico	573	2725	1·74
Jordan	573	2085	1·33
Nicaragua	586	1985	1·24
Algeria	587	2230	1·39
Venezuela	608	2255	1·35
Philippines	631	2145	1·24
Panama	634	2370	1·36
Turkey	656	2650	1·47
Brazil	657	2818	1·57
Colombia	657	2225	1·23
Costa Rica	701	2555	1·33
South Africa	741	2620	1·29
Cuba	776	2870	1·35
Paraguay	817	2355	1·05
Chile	823	2610	1·16
Israel	998	2715	0·99

Source: *Food Balances in Foreign Countries*, U.S.D.A. FAS-M-101, 104, 108, 1960/61 Part, II, III, IV.

There are a few unexpected jumps in the series. The low figures for Bolivia and Nicaragua indicate a high proportion of meat in the diet — though the total calorie intake appears inadequate. The comparatively high figures for the Cameroun and Nigeria, are related to a high proportion of sweet potatoes, yams and cassava in the diet, indicating a possible protein shortage. In Tanganyika, the poorest country, the effect of a certain amount of meat consumption in the pastoral regions is offset by millet consumption elsewhere.

Buck gave detailed data for consumption in 136 separate Chinese villages in the early 1930s. These were likewise ranged in ascending order of calorie consumption, and each tenth village selected for analysis on the same lines, all food consumed being expressed in wheat equivalents by the same international scale as used above (not on Buck's original scale, based on Chinese prices, etc.).

In this case, however, the results did not indicate a declining ratio as the nutrition of a village improved (the range covered was from 1000 to 4000 calorie/person/day). The distinction was rather regional. The average for all the villages surveyed was 2·67 calories/g. wheat equivalent, which was about what was to be expected in relation to the figures for other countries given in the previous table. But for the rice-eating villages the average was only 2·20. A g. of wheat equivalent corresponds to 1·25 g. of rough rice, or 0·92 g. of milled rice, giving 3.32 calories, if we assume milling at the minimum Japanese rate. So it is not rice eating as such, but some other features in the diets of the rice-eating villages — they are in the richer part of China, and consume more meat and fruit — which account for this low figure. There were, however, several villages whose diet consisted predominantly of millet, sorghum and other coarse grains, which appeared to be satisfactory in that it did not include excessively high proportions of root crops, or a low proportion of vegetables. In these villages the calories obtained per g. of wheat equivalent consumed were about equivalent to the full theoretical figure of 3·16 — the calories lost in the consumption of meat, vegetables, etc., were fully made up by the greater cheapness of millet in relation to wheat.

These coarse grains, particularly millet, are dry and difficult to eat. Africans mix leafy vegetables with them to make them more palatable. In many parts of Asia it is regarded as a degradation to have to consume millet instead of rice.

Nevertheless, if we set out to state the physiological minimum requirements of mankind, we must assume that people threatened with an actual shortage of food will be willing to eat millets, etc., and in this way obtain 3·16 calories per g. wheat equivalent consumed. This means that each calorie consumed per day calls for ·01157 kg. wheat equivalent to be consumed per year.

The above analysis enables us to restate more precisely our provisional conclusions on minimum requirements in terms of kg. wheat equivalent per head per year, at 230 for small-bodied people in a hot climate, rising to 275 for fairly large-bodied people (adult males 60 kg.) in a cold climate. Including a minimum requirement of textile fibres, therefore, we can state the minimum agricultural requirements of mankind as ranging from 245 to 290 kg. wheat equivalent/person/year, according to varying climates and body weights: in round figures, a little over a quarter of a ton.

In the advanced communities, on the other hand, we consume about ten times as much, or $2\frac{1}{2}$ tons wheat equivalent/head/year. (The amount actually consumed in the form of cereals is, of course, very small: it is the high proportion of meat, dairy products, etc., in our diet which raises the wheat equivalent.) This appears to be about the maximum beyond which consumption cannot go — you cannot consume less than $\frac{1}{4}$ ton wheat equivalent/head without endangering health, or *more* than $2\frac{1}{2}$ tons — judging by the experience of the United States, where continually rising real income is now accompanied by approximately stationary consumption per head of agricultural produce. (The replacement of fibres of agricultural origin by synthetic fibres has played some part here, too.)

TABLE XI. FOOD CONSUMPTION PER HEAD IN U.S.A.

	Gross income per head $ of 1954 purchasing power	All Agricultural Products expressed as tons of wheat equivalent per head			
		Production	Exports	Imports	Consumption
1909–14	1169	2·55	0·38	0·32	2·48
1920–24	1219	2·63	0·44	0·47	2·41
1925–29	1440	2·39	0·35	0·45	2·49
1930–34	1142	2·25	0·24	0·37	2·38
1935–39	1360	2·31	0·20	0·41	2·52
1952–54	2265	2·77	0·24	0·33	2·86
1955–58	2364	2·79	0·34	0·31	2·77

These figures of food consumption per head, measured in wheat equivalents, must not of course be confused with *total agricultural production* per head, also measured in wheat equivalents, which was the variable which de Vries had in mind. Production differs from consumption to the extent that food is imported or exported; and even subsistence communities have a certain amount of non-food agricultural production (cotton, etc.), almost entirely for export. The figures for total agricultural production are re-expressed in kg. of economic wheat equivalent per head of total population and are given in the following table.

TABLE XII.   TOTAL PRODUCT FROM AGRICULTURE
EXPRESSED IN KG. ECONOMIC WHEAT
EQUIVALENT/PERSON/YEAR

	Food	Non-food	Total
NORTH AFRICA			
Algeria	498	137	635
Egypt	410	119	529
Ethiopia	466	23	489
Libya	298	39	337
Morocco	549	44	593
Sudan	556	76	632
Tunisia	489	50	539
REST OF AFRICA			
Angola	358	150	508
Cameroun	387	208	595
Congo and Ruanda Urundi	364	48	412
Former French Equatorial Africa	351	61	412
Former French West Africa (excl. Guinea)	356	72	428
Ghana	393	244	637
Guinea	344	7	351
Kenya	405	58	463
Liberia	325	177	502
Nigeria and British Cameroons	476	31	507
Rhodesia and Nyasaland	390	124	514
South Africa	871	150	1021
Tanganyika	334	92	426
Togo	370	96	466
NEAR EAST			
Iran	529	45	574
Iraq	653	47	700
Israel	794	32	826
Jordan	431	4	435
Lebanon	315	17	332
Syria	491	195	686
Turkey	680	108	788
FAR EAST			
Burma	567	22	589
Ceylon	377	241	618
India	346	36	382
Indonesia	465	60	525
Japan	504	36	540
Malaya	410	543	953

	Food	Non-food	Total
Pakistan	372	60	432
Philippines	678	32	710
South Korea	418	17	435
Taiwan	619	33	652
Thailand	587	65	652
LATIN AMERICA			
Bolivia	397	24	421
Brazil	656	239	895
Chile	761	92	853
Colombia	641	235	876
Costa Rica	782	325	1107
Cuba	1508	96	1604
Dominican Republic	755	180	935
Ecuador	524	91	615
El Salvador	356	315	671
Guatemala	368	162	530
Haiti	341	73	414
Honduras	455	98	553
Mexico	572	149	721
Nicaragua	577	314	891
Panama	641	33	674
Paraguay	856	98	954
Peru	510	105	615
Venezuela	403	82	485

Source: *Food Balances in Foreign Countries*, U.S.D.A. FAS-M-101, 104,
    108, 1960/1, Part II, III, IV.
    FAO Production Yearbook, 1960.

This table shows two countries, Guinea and Libya, quite close
to the subsistence level — although the low Libyan output is now
beginning to be supplemented by oil revenues. (The low figure for
Lebanon does not mean what it appears to mean; this country has
a substantial income from industry and finance, and can afford to
import food.) These are the lowest figures for whole countries; we
can study some lower figures for individual villages, or families, as
will be seen below.

A comparable account of the stages of agricultural development,
from the point of view of an administrator imposing taxation, is
given with some precision by Winter.[1] The first stage which Winter describes as 'pure subsistence' includes what we have defined as
'pre-agricultural' (e.g. the Pygmies and Bushmen), and also the

[1] E. H. Winter, *Bwamba Economy*, East African Institute of Social Research,
1956.

earliest stages of subsistence agriculture, which he tersely defines as 'no cash crops; no tax; no import or export of labour'.

Winter's second stage is defined as 'subsistence with taxes'. Here we have some cash crops grown, and a certain amount of labour going to seek employment elsewhere, for the principal purpose of paying the tax. Administrators have imposed taxes in Africa, not only because they need revenue, but also with the deliberate object of provoking a transition from pure subsistence to a cash economy. It is not for us now to debate the very large question of whether this has been a desirable policy; we may perhaps now be entitled to say that, if there are grounds for applying it, it should nevertheless be applied with great caution and moderation. Winter gives numerous examples of African communities in this stage, such as the peoples of Ruanda Urundi, the Karamoju, the Masai, and the Bukonjo of former French West Africa.

Winter's next stage is defined as 'subsistence plus cash crops', the stage by which taxes have now become a comparatively minor part of total cash outlay, and cash crops are grown with the object of making money for the purchase of a variety of commodities. Such communities seldom have to send men to work away from the district; and at the same time seldom receive labour from other districts. Examples in Africa are the Teso, the Busoga, the Lango, the people of Sekumaland and of Gambia.

The next stage, which Winter defines as 'subsistence plus cash' is, somewhat paradoxically, one in which quite a large proportion of the men do seek work outside the district. The desire for cash expenditure is greater, and the men travel a considerable distance to get fairly high-paid work. Nyasaland, Togoland, and the Kikuyu are examples of this stage.

Winter's fifth and sixth stages are those in which most of the agricultural labour is working for wages, firstly on agricultural plantations (e.g. the Nigerian oil-palm area, or parts of Uganda); later in a fully industrial economy, such as the Rand in South Africa. It must be pointed out, that while certain communities have passed through these stages, they are by no means universal; agricultural development may lead to an economy still mainly dependent on individual and family farmers, as in the United States.

A definite exception to de Vries's generalization, however, appears to be provided by the Hausa of Northern Nigeria. A survey of six villages in the Zaria province[1] showed agricultural production, in kg. grain equivalent/person/year, ranging from 148 to 396 only and a substantial *import* of food from outside the region to bring consumption up to minimum standards. This, however, is a good case of *exceptio probat regulum* — the exception 'proves' the rule in the old sense of the word 'prove', testing its limits and underlying assumptions. The land inhabited by the Hausa is dry savannah, with a short wet season, the only time of the year at which agriculture is possible. Even this is unreliable, and the distribution of the rainfall within the wet season erratic. Millet, a hardy crop, is best able to stand these conditions; but even so the agriculturist cannot be at all sure of his return. Under these circumstances, the Hausa, who are believed in any case to have been the descendants of immigrant nomads from the north, have become considerable practitioners of trades and handicrafts.

The village whose agriculture has been most productive (or perhaps had had the best luck with rainfall in this particular year) produced 396 kg. grain equivalent/person (190 grain and 206 cotton, of which latter 181 were sold). In addition, the men earned an average of 90 units by handicraft and 39 by trade; the women, trading on their own account, as is the West African custom, another 98; the sale of forest products brought in fifteen, and men working outside the village six, or a total of 644 kg. grain equivalent/person in all. Of this, 143 was used to purchase food from outside the village, bringing consumption of farm products up to 358.

The following table gives interesting further details of these six villages (including the one described above) arranged in ascending order of food consumption:

TABLE XIII.   HAUSA CONSUMPTION OF FARM PRODUCTS

Kg. Grain Equivalent/Person/Year

Consumption of						
agricultural products	245	252	293	296	333	538
Non-cereal consumption included above	108	116	113	128	171	163
Agricultural production	188	148	229	362	190	396
Agricultural products sold	51	26	75	136	73	181
Agricultural products purchased	108	130	139	70	216	143

[1] M. G. Smith, *The Economy of Hausa Communities in Zaria*, Colonial Research Study No. 16.

Kg. grain equivalent/ha./year

Grain	724	375	551	702	668	690
Other crops	2670	700	1095	2020	1135	1820
Principal export crop	Ground nuts	None	Cotton	Cotton	Ground nuts and sugar	Cotton
Access to road	No	No	Yes — recent	Near	Yes — old trade route	Yes — all season

The importance of access to transport in facilitating economic development could hardly be shown more clearly.

A study of the economic position of women in Bamenda in the Cameroons[1] shows that population density has risen from 13 persons/sq. km. in 1933 to 15·5 in 1948 and 26 in 1958, i.e. they now have 4 ha./person. However, the amount of land actually cultivated is only 0·18 ha./person (the same in 1948, and 0·15 in 1933), only about one-tenth of the farm land being cultivated in any given year; 16 per cent is used for grazing — but only the roughest grazing 'under range conditions' by cattle belonging to the nomadic Fulani, *not to the local inhabitants*. Responsibility for food production is left to the women who practise a system of rotational grass fallowing; the period varying from two to ten years, depending on availability and accessibility of land. The women (who work about 1200 hours/year on farm crops) obtained a yield of 1566 kg. grain equivalent/ha./year in 1933 (238 kg./person/year); an additional 150 kg./person/year was contributed by a few other men growing coffee for cash. In subsequent years, the area under food crops and coffee was increased; but yield per ha. appears not to have changed. Meanwhile, Fulani cattle trespass had become a major problem, causing widespread destruction of crops (the more numerous the cattle, the greater the income of the Fulani); by 1958 many outlying farms had been abandoned and women were beginning to fence in their crops.[2] In Kaberry's view, the present farming system could be symbiotic with a separate grazing system if it were possible to resolve farmer-grazier relations.

Bamenda, 4,500 feet above sea level, has frequently been cited as one of the most fertile areas of West Africa, with a soil and climate favourable to the production of coffee, pyrethrum, linseed

[1] P. Kaberry, *Women of the Grassfields*: A study of the economic position of women in Bamenda, British Cameroons; Colonial Research Publication No. 14, 1952. Also W. M. Bridges, MS, 1934.
[2] P. Kaberry, *Report on Farmer-Grazier Relations*, London University, mimeographed, April 1959.

and quinine, apart from numerous local food crops. To subsistence cultivators living under such generous conditions of soil and climate the raising of draught oxen must appear a superfluity.

Studies of Uganda villages much more densely populated, show the transition to draught animal cultivation nearly completed.

TABLE XIV. TRANSITION TO DRAUGHT ANIMAL CULTIVATION IN UGANDA VILLAGES

	Moruita[1] 1955	Kasilang[2] 1953	Ajuluka[3] 1937	Opami[3] 1937	Kasilang[2] 1937
Percentage of land hand-cultivated	1	5	5	28	29
Ha./person:					
Total land area	1·12	1·73	1·82	3·19	2·10
Cultivable land	0·85	1·17	1·49	3·15	1·33
Cultivated	0·68	0·52	0·52	0·52	0·52
Production kg. grain equivalent/person/year					
Food crops	360	298	303	331	293
Cash crops	296	195	320	204	278
Total	656	493	623	535	571
Production do., net of grain fed to draught oxen	621	447	580	504	525
Draught oxen/person	0·21	0·28	0·26	0·79	0·28
Ha. grazing/person	0	0	0·40	0·34	0

The ploughs in Moruita appeared to be underpowered, and more oxen (and more grain to feed to them) necessary.

The situation in India and Pakistan is illustrated by data for the hill and submontane regions of the Punjab.[4] On farms averaging 1·11 ha./person (8·0 persons/family), after providing for the feeding of livestock, they produce 439 kg. grain equivalent/person/year, of which as much as 225 is milk. Livestock holdings per family average 3·4 draught oxen, 2·6 milch cattle, and 1·7 young stock. The average farm feeds to livestock 2280 kg./year of grain and similar foods, together with 1170 kg./year of grain equivalent of fodder crops and roughages, or 4050 kg./year in all, of which 1368 is to 2·6 milch cattle (who together yield 1519 kg./year milk).

The Punjab, however, is one of the most agriculturally advanced regions of the whole sub-continent, with holdings of livestock much higher than the average.

[1] P. N. Wilson, 'An Agricultural Survey of Moruita Erony, Teso', *Uganda Journal*, Vol. 22, No. 1, March 1958.
[2] P. N. Wilson and J. M. Watson, 'Two Surveys of Kasilang Erony, Teso', *Uganda Journal*, Vol. 20, No. 2, September 1956.
[3] M. G. de Courcy-Ireland, H. R. Hosking and L. J. A. Loewenthal, *An Investigation into Health and Agriculture in Teso, Uganda*, Entebbe, 1937.
[4] *Family Budgets of Nineteen Cultivators in the Punjab, 1953–54*, Punjab Board of Economic Enquiry, Publication No. 39.

CHAPTER V

Production and Productivity

It is almost true to say that stationariness of agricultural production, or rather agricultural production increasing only at the same rate as population, is the characteristic mark of a peasant community. Eighteenth-century France,[1] though somewhat chivvied by Britain, was nevertheless the greatest military and commercial power of the time, and the world's scientific and cultural centre. However, it was still essentially a peasant economy, and from the beginning of the eighteenth century to 1790 the average rate of growth of agricultural product was only 0·5 per cent a year, as compared with the population growth of 0·2 per cent a year.[2] If we covered the whole period from the beginning of the eighteenth century to the end of the Napoleonic Wars we would get a still lower figure; but it might be contended that this was including an unduly large proportion of war years per century.

Goldsmith[3] found for Russia for the period 1860–1913, i.e. even during the period of railway construction and the first steps of industrialization, agricultural production growing at 2 per cent a year, as against population growing 1½ per cent a year. De Vries has contended that, in a real subsistence economy, it can almost be taken as a law of nature that agricultural production will increase at about the same rate as population. Any slower — or faster — growth would cause unbearable social strains.

For Indonesia[4] we have an estimate of milled-rice consumption per head at 115 kg. for 1836. During the nineteenth century cassava was introduced into Indonesia. On the FAO scale of kg., cassava

[1] J. C. Toutain, *Le Produit de l'Agriculture Française de 1700 a 1958*, Vol. II, Cahiers de l'Institut de Science Economique Appliqué, Supplement No. 115, July 1961.
[2] The higher figures for both production and population given by Toutain on p. 204 of his report appear to be for an area which was territorially enlarging. The figures quoted above are estimated for a constant area. Territorial enlargements during the eighteenth century (Lorraine and Corsica) are quoted by Toutain on p. 24 of the first volume of his report, and they added 7·4 per cent to the area of France. It is assumed that the population change was in the same proportion.
[3] International Association for Research in Income and Wealth, Hindsgavl Conference, 1955.
[4] Van der Koppel, *De Landbouw in den Indischen Archipel*.

is worth 0·194 kg. milled rice, which appears to give an adequate representation of its value as a food. This coefficient is used in the following table.

RICE AND CASSAVA CONSUMPTION IN INDONESIA, KG./PERSON/YEAR

	Rice	Cassava	Combined consumption expressed as rice equivalents	Protein from these sources g./person/day
1836	115	0	115	31
1913	102	71	116	29
1936–40	86	159	117	27

During this period however a substantial production of sugar, tea, rubber and other commercial crops was introduced. The protein supply obtained from rice and cassava was not adequate, even on Professor Waterlow's standards; a certain amount of protein may have been obtained from other sources. Additional production in Indonesia in the latter period, of crops grown little or not at all in 1836, in kg. of milled rice equivalent per head of population (information from Java only) was 34 of other staples (maize and sweet potatoes) and 64 of 'commercial' crops (principally sugar and rubber, with some soya beans, groundnuts, copra, coffee, tea and tobacco).

Even in eighteenth-century England, the supposed classical case of an economic 'take-off', total real product per head of population[1] was estimated to be increasing at only 0·3 per cent per year between 1700 and 1770, 0·6 per cent from 1770 to 1800; and during these periods productive manufacturing industries and commerce were playing a rapidly increasing part in national output, so that the rate of growth of agricultural productivity per head must have been substantially less than these.

Germany between 1800 and 1883[2] provides an example of the next stage of development. During this period the rate of population growth averaged 0·8 per cent per year, higher than in the eighteenth century. Agricultural production increased at the rate of 1·1 per cent per year, still only a small lead over population. Between 1883 and 1900 the rate of growth of agricultural production accelerated to 2·1 per cent per year, while the rate of popula-

---

[1] P. Deane and W. A. Cole, 'The Long Term Growth of the United Kingdom', International Association for Research in Income and Wealth Conference, 1959.
[2] Bitterman, *Die Landwirtschaftliche Produktion in Deutschland, 1800–1950.*

tion growth had risen to 1·2 per cent per year. This increased agricultural production, relative to population, not only enabled everyone to eat rather better, but also set free resources to enable an increased proportion of the population to work in industry and other non-agricultural employments, which occupied only a quarter of the population in 1800, 59 per cent in 1883, and 68 per cent in 1900.

No European example however can match the extraordinary achievement of Japan. The modernization of the Japanese economy began with a single dramatic event in 1868, the counter-revolution against the nobility and samurai and the resumption of power by the Emperor Meiji. For the better part of the previous two centuries, the Tokugawa period, the emperors had been ciphers in a country entirely ruled by the nobility, a country[1] of 'virtually stationary population of 28 to 30 millions, pressed close to the limits of subsistence afforded by the simple rice economy of the coastal plains and mountain valleys, with its restricted commerce and handicrafts and burdensome exactions of feudal aristocracy'.

After the Meiji restoration a population growth at the rate of about 1 per cent per annum began. Japanese historians point out that much of this change should be explained by the cessation of the practice of infanticide. But Japan showed a capacity for increasing agricultural production at a very much greater rate. Lockwood has assembled sufficient information[2] (the Japanese have always been very good at keeping statistics) to construct index numbers of agricultural and fishery output back to the period 1885–9. For most of the period the data can be reweighted to FAO units to make them fully comparable with all our other information. In the decade beginning 1885–9 Japanese agricultural production was growing at the rate of 2·3 per cent a year. From 1905 onwards it was growing at the rate of 3·5 per cent per year, which appears to have been the highest rate of growth of agricultural product of any country in the world at that time. This high rate of growth was continued into the 1920s, after which it was checked, primarily by the collapse in the market for silk, then one of Japan's most important agricultural products.

Long-period historical index numbers of agricultural production are available for much of the nineteenth century for many of the

---

[1] W. W. Lockwood, *The Economic Development of Japan*, O.U.P., 1955.
[2] See also E. F. Penrose, *Food Supply and Raw Materials in Japan*, Chicago, 1930.

F

advanced countries — but they are not our concern at the moment. Not much information is available for countries in an early stage of development. The available data are given on the following diagram.[1] Soviet Russia, which was going to solve the problem of

CHART I. AGRICULTURAL PRODUCT GRAPH

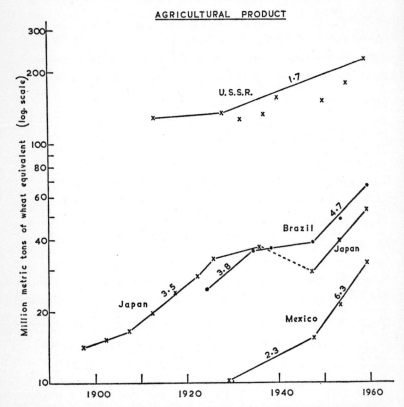

agricultural growth by collectivization, has only managed to secure a rate of growth of 1·7 per cent a year when measured between 1928 and 1959, even less if the measurement is based on 1913.

Brazil and Mexico look like matching the achievements of Japan. It must, however, be remembered that agricultural expansion has been much easier in the case of these countries with abundant

[1] Data for Soviet Union from *The Real Product of Soviet Russia*, U.S. Senate Committee on the Judiciary, U.S. Government Printing Office, 1961. Other countries from 1935–9, *FAO Production Indexes*. Earlier data for Brazil compiled from information in *International Institute of Agriculture Yearbook*. 1929 index for Mexico from *Commercio Exterior*, September 1957.

vacant land, as compared with Japan, already densely populated at the beginning of the period. Brazilian agriculture however was very dependent on coffee production, and suffered a serious check with the heavy fall in coffee prices in the 1930s, which led the Brazilian government to impose deliberate restrictions on coffee production. Subject to this check in the 1930s, Brazil, however, has shown high rates of increase. But very few countries have shown a rate of increase like that of Mexico during the 1950s. Mexican population growth during the 1950s was at the rate of 3·1 per cent a year; but agricultural growth greatly exceeded this.

TABLE XV. GROWTH-RATES PER CENT PER YEAR — AGRICULTURAL PRODUCTION AND POPULATION

	Agricultural 1934–38 to 1959–60	Production 1953–54 to 1959–60	Population 1936 to 1960
Israel		9·8	7·0
Guatemala		4·6	2·6
Iran		3·3	0·9
Panama		3·2	2·7
Turkey	3·2		2·2
Colombia	3·0		2·2
Thailand	3·0		2·6
Venezuela		2·7	2·9
Cuba	2·3		2·0
Ceylon	2·3		2·3
Philippines	2·2		2·6
South Africa	2·2		2·1
Honduras		2·1	2·6
Tunisia	2·1		2·0
Peru	2·0		2·1
Malaya	2·0		2·4
Taiwan	1·7		2·9
Morocco	1·7		2·1
Egypt	1·6		2·1
India	1·3		1·5
Chile	1·2		1·8
Indonesia	1·2		1·4
South Korea	0·9		2·1
Pakistan	0·7		1·5
Algeria	0·5		1·7
Ethiopia		0·4	1·6
Burma	− 0·2		1·2
Syria		− 0·2	2·6
Iraq		− 0·3	2·7

Rates computed from FAO Index Numbers of Agricultural Production.

For other low-income countries we only have the FAO index numbers for the rate of growth from the base period 1934–8 to the three years centred on 1959–60 (using data for a single year gives very unreliable results because of fluctuations in the weather). In a number of cases we have data only for the period beginning with the three years centred on 1953–4.

Israel's agricultural achievement greatly surpasses even its high rate of population growth. A number of other countries have shown their capacity to increase at rates in the neighbourhood of 3 per cent per year. It is disquieting, however, to see the figures for India, and the countries below her in the list, whose agricultural production has been increasing at a slower rate than population, whether through war and banditry (Indonesia, Algeria, Burma), runaway currency inflation (Chile, South Korea) or other reasons. (We need not however have any anxiety about Iraq, which now has plenty of oil revenues to take the place of agriculture.)

Lockwood points to the most spectacular feature of Japanese economic growth — the very rapid growth of industry after the turn of the century. With large numbers moving into industry, incentives to the cultivator were sustained by the supplies of textiles, hardware, building materials, etc., available to him at low prices. More significant than the aggregate growth in the Japanese economy, however, was the sustained rise in the efficiency of labour. In farming, most of the efficiency gain was the result of simple scientific improvements, plant breeding, increased irrigation and use of fertilizers; in industry the productivity of labour advanced more rapidly with the harnessing of mechanical energy to industrial pursuits. But the gain in transport efficiency, measured in human effort, Lockwood regards as the outstanding case of saving labour on a massive scale — and the availability of transport enabled labour and capital to be combined and concentrated in various specialized ways, resulting in the exchange of surpluses in widely organized markets.

The Mexican revolution of 1910 transformed a semi-feudal economy into one of rapid economic growth, following distribution of land to peasants, and the spread of education. (Nationalization of oil and the railroads came later, in the 1930s: an international crisis over the expropriation of foreign property was narrowly avoided.) Since 1940 there has been a boom reminiscent of the great expansion in the United States in the nineteenth century. This expansion in the economy from 1940 is partly explained by the close co-operation between the United States and Mexico with heavy U.S. investment, the annual migration of Mexican agricultural workers to the States, and the exchange of students and technicians; in addition Mexico is very dependent upon the U.S. tourist trade to stabilize its economy.

Urban centres of modern commerce and secondary industry with relatively large wage-earning populations have developed as a direct result of the rapid expansion of cash-crop production in Africa; the outstanding feature of the increased product is, however, that it has mainly been used to purchase imports — also a notable feature of the Japanese economy in early stages of development.

But in India agricultural product per head shows a slight decrease when comparing 1960 with 1931–2. The subsistence sector remains massive. Despite intensive application of labour, crop yields remain among the lowest in the world, with the persistence of traditional techniques of production.

We may well examine in more detail the nature of this agricultural growth beyond subsistence level. In the normal course of events, we should expect it to be in livestock products or crops other than the subsistence crops (cereals and roots). This is however not always the case — a country may continue to expand its production of subsistence crops beyond its own requirements, and export some of them.

The method used in the following table is to record the output of all these non-subsistence products, converted into wheat equivalents, in kg. per head of population. A conventional allowance of 250 kg. wheat equivalent for subsistence is made at the end of the table. Exports of subsistence products are added in and, in some cases, imports debited. This method is not merely for the purpose of saving a certain amount of arithmetic, in compiling the data for the subsistence crops; it is also because of the fact that in many of these countries information on the output of the subsistence crops, and still more, of the quantities used for seed and animal feeding, which should be excluded from estimates of final agricultural output, are much less accurately known than we might wish. The subsistence figure is meant to include the wheat equivalent of fruits and vegetables, which may be consumed in fairly large quantities by subsistence populations, and of whose output we have very little accurate information.

TABLE XVI. PRODUCTION OTHER THAN CEREALS, ROOTS, FRUITS AND VEGETABLES FOR LOCAL SUBSISTENCE, IN KG. WHEAT EQUIVALENT/HEAD OF POPULATION/YEAR

	Year	Meat	Milk	Wool	Eggs	Silk	Fish	Sugar	Tea	Coffee	Cocoa	Jute	Cotton	Tobacco	Other crops	Net imports (−) or exports (+) of cereals and roots	Total	Add 250 (assumed) for subsistence	Population m.	Total Product (m. metric tons wheat equivalent)	Do. in present day boundaries
China[1]	1933	31			6		8	1	1				11	4	8	+ 2	68	318	500	159	
,,	1955-6	28			4		15	1	1				15	4	6	+ 4	71	321	628	202	
India[2]	1931-2[a]	10	75	1	1		8	13	5			9	12	9	24	− 7	158	408	271		433
,,	1960	29	63	1	1		5	16	7			6	13	5	26	− 12	142	392	433		
Philippines[3]	1935-7				4		45	78		1				21	63	− 12	228	478	12.8		
Iraq[4]	1895-9	84	37	21									1	1	59	+ 35	242	492	3.55		
Japan[5]	1900-4		0.7		3	20	43	6	6					7		− 1	83	333	42.7	14.2	
,,	1905-9		0.9		3	23	46	5	5					7			89	339	45.2	15.3	
,,	1910-14		1		5	26	51	2	5				1	7		− 1	97	347	48.1	16.7	
,,	1915-19		1		6	32	88	3	6					7		− 3	133	383	51.3	19.6	
,,	1920-4		1		7	43	123	3	5					9		− 16	189	439	54.9	24.1	
,,	1925-7		2		8	44	173	2	5					8		− 20	229	479	58.8	28.2	
,,	1934-8		6		16	75	219	1	6					7		− 33	293	543	61.7	33.5	
Syria[4]	1934-5	57	92	22	7	4	(10)	9					8	6	122	− 28	291	541	69.0	37.3	
Egypt[4]	1934-5	78	39	7	7		(10)						153	10	307	− 13	315	565	3.4		
Palestine[4]	1934-5	23	106	17	17		(10)							6		+ 1	318	568	15.3		
Sweden[6]	1861-5	100	261		5	2	(20)	4					18	18	101	− 89	385	635	1.23		
Turkey[4]	1934-5	88	157	15	14	5	(5)						18	11	270	+ 30	406	656	4.0		
Cyprus[4]	1934-5	76	46	14	18		(25)	6					11	11	11	+ 11	445	695	16.0	0.366	
Yugoslavia[7]	1939	172	180	9	15	6	6	21						7		− 22	450	700	15.8		
,, [b]		48	138													+ 33	441	691			
,, [c]		138	315		51																
Brazil[8]	1924-5	375	79	4	5		(10)	49		144	8		25	14	36	− 17	484	734	34	25.0	
,,	1934-5	127	77	5	7		(10)	60		225	14		48	20	43	− 23	631	881	41	36.1	
,,	1938-9	145	76	5	9		(10)	63		168	14		63	18	35	− 20	590	840	44	37.0	
U.S.S.R.[9]	1913	149	230	9	12		18	18	9				10	5	11	+ 69	572	822	139.3	114.5	129
,,	1928	188	262	13	18		26	9	9				16	6	22	+ 7	545	795	151.4	120.4	135
,,	1932	179	170	5	7		18	8	6				8	8	29	+ 20	468	718	158.1	113.5	138
,,	1937	177	205	7	13		30	9	8				21	13	28	+ 19	472	722	165.1	112.2	128
,,	1940[d]	106	177	10	16		34	11	13				43	12	33	+ 71	549	799	198.0	158.2	133
,,	1950	173	188	13	18		33	14	13				39	13	36	+ 57	557	807	186.3	150.3	
,,	1955	144	223	13	24		48	18	14					14	64	+ 30	656	906	199.0	180.3	
,,	1959	182	318	17	32		55	29	19				41	19	61	+ 24	838	1088	210.5	229.0	

[a] Excluding Princely States and Burma.   [b] Kosmet (most densely populated area).   [c] Voivodina (least densely populated area).   [d] Boundary change.

[1] For 1933: J. L. Buck, Land Utilization in China. For 1955-6: MS in course of publication.
[2] V. K. V. R. Rao, The National Income of British India, 1931-32, London, 1940.   [3] International Institute of Agriculture Yearbook.
[4] Bonné, Economic Development of the Middle East, 1943.   [5] W. W. Lockwood, The Economic Development of Japan, O.U.P., 1955.
[6] Myrdal and others, The National Income of Sweden, 1861 to 1930.   [7] Mihailović, World Population Conference, 1954.
[8] Data for Soviet Russia from The Real Product of Soviet Russia, U.S. Senate Committee on the Judiciary, U.S. Government Printing Office, 1961. Other countries from 1935–9, FAO Production Indexes. Earlier data for Brazil compiled from information in International Institute of Agriculture Yearbook. 1929 index for Mexico from Commercio Exterior, September 1957.

Considerable diversities in the pattern are noticeable. Milk, for instance, is completely absent in China and the Philippines, virtually absent in Japan. It is almost as important a product in India as it is in Brazil. It plays a larger part in the cooler climates, particularly Sweden and Russia. Supplies of meat seem to go up as the economy advances, subject to the important qualification that Japan and the Philippines, with their comparatively large supplies of fish, need less meat on that account. Eggs never form a large part of output in such countries. The other crops, apart from tobacco which is widely grown round the world, tend to be specialized to the countries which are climatically suited to them, except for silk, which could have been grown in a variety of climates, but which flourished in Japan due to the long experience of the people, and their low wages.

From these figures of national agricultural product, necessarily limited to countries for which reasonably good national statistics are available, we now turn to information on productivity based on general local observation, or studies of individual farms, or groups of farms. To have such information in the form merely of round-figure general averages is a useful start: but it is much more interesting if we are able to compare farms at different levels of labour input/ha., so that we can estimate the marginal productivity of labour, or of land. These procedures have not yet been carried out satisfactorily in any great number of cases by agricultural economists even in the advanced countries, and we must be content with rough and ready measurements. Nevertheless, they are of great interest and importance. Finally, we can test our results by applying the basic economic theorem, that the wage paid to hired agricultural labourers should be approximately equal to the marginal product of labour.

We may begin by considering some information from the ancient world. In ancient Greece, the normal wheat yield in Attica in the late fourth century B.C. was estimated[1] at 0·9 tons/ha. Michell points out that much higher yields were obtained in Egypt, Babylonia and Sicily. For ancient Egypt a figure of 2 tons/ha. has been estimated.[2]

To give the background of these figures we may note that in modern Greece in 1934–8 the figure was only 0·9 tons/ha., in

---

[1] Michell, *The Economics of Ancient Greece.*
[2] A. C. Johnson's volume on Egypt in the series, *Economic Survey of the Roman Empire.*

India only 0·65. The Egyptian figure had fallen to 1·4 by 1830, the first year for which we have modern information, and it is only recently that it has risen again to the 2 tons/ha. of ancient times.

In mediaeval England productivity was even lower, and progress very slow:

Wheat Yields, Tons/Ha.

Year	Gross[1]	Net after seed[1]	Gross[2]
1250	—	—	0·43
1350	0·54	0·37	0·56
1450	0·57	0·40	—
1550	0·64	0·47	1·06
1650	0·74	0·57	—
1750	1·01	0·84	1·41
1850	1·8	1·6	1·8

Over a large part of the world to-day agricultural productivity is now the same as, or even inferior to, what it was in the leading civilized communities 2,000 years ago. This is the system of agriculture described in most interesting detail in the poetry of Hesiod and Virgil. Its basic technique was ploughing and harrowing with teams of oxen — somewhat slow and clumsy, but very much more efficient than that of the bronze-age agriculture which had preceded it. Its essential implement, it need hardly be pointed out, was the iron ploughshare, a fairly recent discovery in Hesiod's time (seventh century B.C.). This was only available in communities which enjoyed not only a knowledge of iron working, but reasonably abundant supplies of this truly precious metal, and the dissemination of them to every village community. In the modern world, 1 lb. of iron exchanges against a little more than 1 lb. of wheat; in the seventh century B.C. it exchanged against some 15 lb. of wheat — but it was well worth it when the alternative was ploughing with a clumsy and short-lived wooden ploughshare.

Customary rice yields in most parts of Asia[3] over the last 50 years have been in the neighbourhood of 1 ton milled rice/ha., with a tendency on the whole to decline, as cultivation was extended into less suitable lands, without fertilizer, and with some (though probably not very serious) soil deterioration. India, Ceylon and

---

[1] M. K. Bennett, 'British Wheat Yield per Acre for Seven Centuries', *Economic History*, February, 1935.

[2] Richardson, *Outlook on Agriculture*, Winter 1960.

[3] Wickizer and Bennett, *The Rice Economy of Monsoon Asia*, California, 1941.

Philippines have shown even lower yields. A figure of 0·9 tons prevailed in Japan a thousand years ago: by the sixteenth century it stood at 1·4. When the modern advance began, in the 1870s, it stood at about 1·7,[1] it now stands at 3·45 (average of last three years' yields, and assuming 72½ per cent extraction). Taking 225 kg. *milled* rice (72½ per cent extraction) as the per head subsistence requirement (including a certain amount to be exchanged for required agricultural products besides rice) for an Asian population, the area of land required to produce this amount is as follows, under varying circumstances:

India in 1930s (Cambodia or Nepal now)	0·27 ha.
India now	0·22 ha.
Japan now	0·06 ha.

The possibility is clearly open to India of supporting a much larger population on the same land, if plant breeding and fertilization can be carried as far as they have been in Japan.

The large part played by fish in the output of Japan, and to a lesser extent of the Philippines, has already been noticed. A representative seaside village in Malaya,[2] though part of its output was for sale to inland villages, had a fish output of 360 kg. (liveweight) per head of the whole village population. FAO recently have drawn attention[3] to the very high yields which can be obtained from cultivated ponds, ranging from 1 ton liveweight fish/ha./year in Indonesia to 1·65 in Israel and 2 in the Belgian Congo. (The highest recorded natural yield of fish was 0·8 in Lake Tempe, Indonesia: some lakes in Egypt yield 0·1 and 0·2; but most natural lakes are much lower yielding; for Lake Victoria the estimate is only ·002.) Cultivating fish in the rice fields at the time when they are under water, by introducing the fish fry, and feeding them, has been said to give a yield of 2·25 tons/ha./year in Japan. A pond at Jos in Nigeria[4] was said to yield 2½ tons, and a similar claim has been made by the Chinese, but it has been disputed.[5] A case has been quoted in Thailand, where perhaps the village refuse is particularly appetizing, of 3 tons.[6] Even if only half of these claims

---

[1] Wickizer and Bennett, op. cit. Also confirmed by Ike, *Journal of Economic History*, 1947.

[2] Firth, *Malay Fishermen, Their Peasant Economy*, Institute of Pacific Relations, 1946.

[3] *Fish Farming and Inland Fishery Management*, 1954.

[4] F. J. Pedler, *The Economic Geography of West Africa*, London, 1955.

[5] Billings, *Annual Review of Plant Physiology*, Vol. VIII, p. 375, 1957.

[6] J. E. de Young, *Village Life in Modern Thailand*, 1955.

are accepted, it is clear that these densely populated countries have a means of obtaining high protein food at a very high rate per unit of area. At any rate in high rainfall countries, the amount of land which could be converted into fishponds is quite high — although they might not be so productive if the village drainage had to be divided among more of them. But it is clear that the capital requirement for constructing a pond, and the labour and pumping equipment for maintaining it, put it beyond the reach of a poor family. In Siam, in addition, a substantial tax is levied on each cubic m. of fishpond.

This information so far has referred to yields per unit area only; we now consider data showing in addition average returns per man-hour of labour input. We have an interesting case of intensive livestock keeping in Africa.[1] The island of Ukara in Lake Victoria (mentioned in Chapter III) is inhabited by 16,500 people at a density of 4·7 persons/ha. cultivable land. Gourou thinks that it was only the *force majeure* of having to live on such a small island in order to escape their enemies which led them to cultivate with such un-African intensiveness. Dairy cattle are kept with an average yield of 3 tons milk/year. Each ha. provides food, including good milk and meat rations, for 4·7 people, indicating a yield of 3000–4000 kg. grain equivalent/ha./year. The average return to men's labour appears to be well above 1 kg. grain equivalent/man-hour, and the marginal return to be fairly high too.

Schweng[2] quotes a study by Sol Tax of men growing maize with hand hoes in the remote hill regions of Guatemala, where each man cultivates on the average three-quarters of a hectare in the season, devoting 87 man-days of labour to it (assuming an eight-hour day, this represents a labour input of 940 man-hours/ha., well below our presumed limit). The yield is at the unexpectedly high rate of 2·75 tons/ha., or 2·92 kg./man-hour.

Beckett[3] found in Africa in the 1930s, when maize cost 1d./lb. and farmers were selling their cocoa at only 1·48d./lb. (on the FAO scale of values cocoa is worth six times maize), their average return per day worked (7 hours) was only equivalent to 5·8 kg. maize (8·8 for work on bearing farms; but much work has to be done on non-bearing bushes).

For East Africa we are fortunate in having a pioneer study of the

[1] P. Gourou, *Annuaire de College de France*, 1961, p. 248.
[2] Private communication.
[3] *Akosoaso*, London School of Economics Monograph on Social Anthropology, No. 10.

TABLE XVII. GENERAL ESTIMATES OF AFRICAN PRODUCTIVITIES

	General Estimate for all Africa[1]				Nyasaland 1938[2] Kg. wheat equivalent/man-hours[b]			Ghana[3]			
	Labour input[a] man-hours /ha.	Crop kg. /ha.	Kg. wheat equivalent /ha.	/man. hours	Hill village	Foothill village	Lake village	Labour input[a] man-hours /ha.	Crop kg. /ha.	Kg. wheat equivalent /ha.	/man. hours
Maize	900	1790	1340	1·49	1·19	0·86		650	712	533	0·81
Eleusine millet	500	953	650	1·30	0·08	0·28					
Cotton (unginned)	1095	462	1358	1·24		0·26					
Groundnut (shelled)	1515	1116	2040	1·35			0·94				
Cassava	1870	14280	3285	1·75			3·39				
Sweet potato	1160	6080	1824	1·58							
Yams	2320	9790						1665	9850	4660[c]	2·96
Beans						0·41					
Rice (rough)		795	646			0·45					
Tobacco (dry leaf)		392	3135								

[a] Assuming 6½ hours/day.
[b] Expressing women, children, infirm men, etc., as 'first-class men' equivalent.
[c] Converted on local prices for maize and yams, which are more favourable to yams than is indicated by their relative nutritive value.

[1] J. W. Y. Higgs, R. K. Kerkham, and J. R. Raeburn, *Report of a Survey of Problems in the Mechanization of Native Agriculture in Tropical African Colonies*, Colonial Office, 1950.
[2] B. S. Platt, *Nutrition Survey*, Colonial Office library, mimeographed.
[3] *Gold Coast Department of Agriculture Yearbook*, 1930, p. 226.

1930s.[1] At a time when 1s. would buy 15 kg. of maize (a quite exceptionally low price — high transport costs kept East African maize prices well below world price, which itself was then very low) the *gross* returns, expressed in kg. maize equivalent/hour, ranged from 2·0 for groundnuts (in the year in question which was very dry, the return was half this, but 2 is regarded as normal), to 2·1 for cassava, and 2·6 for sorghum or cotton. There are several factors explaining this much higher level of productivity, as compared with West Africa; the soil is rich, whereas West African soils are deficient in phosphorus; the climate is more favourable, with a shorter dry season. On the other hand, Couchman was examining the records of farmers who still worked with hand hoes. Male and female labour was used in approximately equal quantities, and he computed his averages without distinguishing between them.

Some general estimates of African productivities have been made by Raeburn, which can be compared with certain other data.[2]

In a thorough survey in a village in Gambia, to which a whole year was devoted, one of the authors obtained results much below Raeburn's figures (both climate and soils in Gambia, however, are less favourable than in many regions of Africa).[3]

TABLE XVIII.   GAMBIA: AVERAGE RETURNS TO LABOUR
IN KG. PER MAN-HOUR

	Actual Returns	Wheat equivalents (FAO weights)
Late millet	·47	·32
Early millet	·48	·33
Sorghum	1·06	·64
Digitaria exilis	·99	·67
Maize	·91	·68
Rough rice: swamp[a]	·64	·51
upland[b]	·17	·14
Groundnuts (unshelled)	·84	·91

[a] flood irrigated.   [b] entirely rainfed.

Relative prices in the local markets appear to have been similar to the FAO relative weights, except that rice was priced locally ex-

[1] Fuggles Couchman, *East African Journal of Agriculture*, March 1939; and Clayton, *Journal of Agricultural Economics*, May 1961.

[2] J. W. Y. Higgs, R. K. Kerkham, and J. R. Raeburn, *Report of a Survey of Problems in the Mechanization of Native Agriculture in Tropical African Colonies*, Colonial Office, 1950.

[3] M. R. Haswell, *Economics of Agriculture in a Savannah Village*, Colonial Research Studies No. 8, 1953.

tremely high relative to the other crops. Regarding the marked differences shown in returns per hour, favoured soils for growing groundnuts are rather scarce, and farmers are reluctant to extend

CHART II.

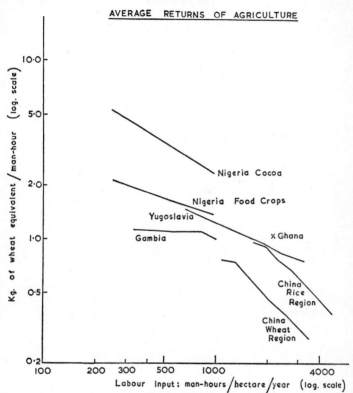

AVERAGE RETURNS OF AGRICULTURE

their groundnut plots to the less well-drained soils to which these give way. Maize can only be grown on very limited areas of land near the houses where domestic animals roam and manure is available. Digitaria and, to a less extent, sorghum are unpalatable, and limited amounts are grown each year as famine reserves. The comparatively high return from swamp rice has indeed led to a great expansion of its production in the ten years since the first survey; though this extension has only been made possible by the building of causeways into the swamp. The growing of the unremunerative upland rice continues, the work being done entirely by the women, who appear to calculate the return to their labour less nicely than the men.

We may now examine those data giving comparisons between farms with varying inputs, from which we can estimate marginal productivities of labour and of land.

CHART III.

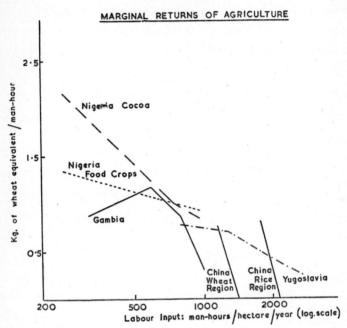

Notes and Sources to the diagrams, average returns of agriculture and marginal returns of agriculture

CHINA: Buck, *Land Utilization in China*, Statistical Supplement, pp. 298, 302.

	Wheat Region		Rice Region
Crop ha./man equivalent	Tons grain equivalent/man equivalent	Crop ha./man equivalent	Tons grain equivalent/man equivalent
0·70	0·68	0·51	0·94
1·00	0·96	0·72	1·33
1·26	1·18	0·88	1·65
1·54	1·44	1·05	1·87
1·98	1·86	1·27	2·26
2·33	1·93	1·55	2·43

(For conversion to man-hours, assumed 2500 worked per year)

GAMBIA: Haswell, *Economics of Agriculture in a Savannah Village*, Colonial Office Research Study no. 8, 1953, p. 56. and Haswell: *The changing pattern of economic activity in a Gambia Village*, Department of Technical Co-operation Overseas Research Publication No. 2, 1963.

1 kg. undecorticated groundnuts equated to 1·3 kg. grain: refers to the cash crop grown by the men.

Data: Man-hours per ha. per year

Man-hours per ha. per year	322	570	817	1065
Grain equivalent per man-hour, kg.:				
Average	1·13	1·10	1·10	0·98
Marginal	0·88	1·18	0·88	0·30

Hours averaged 6 per day (the women cultivating rice generally working a little longer than the men) and farm work is only performed for some 9 months of the year, because nothing useful can be done in the dry season February-April. Allowing for some rest days, the total labour input per worker is only about 1350 hours per year.

GHANA: Privately communicated by Mr. Torto, Deputy Director of Agriculture.

Itinerant maize growers on worn-out cocoa lands cultivate (with hand tools) 0·8 ha. per man, cropping two times a year, obtaining 1820 kg. of maize in all. Average man-hours per year assumed 1750.

NIGERIA: Galetti, Baldwin and Dina, *Nigerian Cocoa Farmers*, p. 337.

Hours per acre per year	Cocoa Farms Average	Cocoa Farms Marginal	Food Crops Average	Food Crops Marginal
100	3·16	1·30	1·28	0·80
200	2·11	0·87	1·02	0·67
300	1·66	0·60	0·89	0·60
400	1·38	0·50	0·81	0·55

One shilling is equated to 1·68 kg. maize, the most common local grain (p. 419). The price of cocoa at the time of the investigation (1951–2) was, per unit of weight, 5·3 times the price of maize. Equations were established (pp. 314, 328) showing:

Yield in lb. cocoa = $53.54 \text{ Acreage}^{.675} \text{ Man-hours}^{.325}$

Food crop yield/acre, shillings, before debiting seed =
$$5.78 \text{ (man-hours/acre)}^{0.67}$$
Food crop yield/acre, shillings, after debiting seed =
$$2.68 \text{ (man-hours/acre)}^{0.76}$$
Food crop yield/acre, thousand calories, before debiting seed =
$$(7238 \text{ man-hours/acre})^{0.5}$$

The relative prices of the different crops do *not* vary according to their calorie content: cassava, per thousand calories, is the least liked, lowest priced and lowest protein crop. Comparing one equation with the other, the money value per thousand calories is found to *rise* (i.e. a tendency to grow a greater proportion of high protein and more palatable products) as labour input per unit rises. Wages averaged

7d. (cocoa farms 7·4, food crops 6·6) per hour, i.e. 0·98 kg. of maize or 2·94 tons per man-year. This is about the marginal product of both cocoa and food crops at a density of 10 labour units per sq. km.

	All work	Farm work
Average hours of work per year: males	1309	1112
females	1552	164

YUGOSLAVIA: Paper by Bicanic at International Association for Income and Wealth Conference, De Pietersberg, 1957.

		Size of holdings in ha.			
	Under 2	2–3	3–5	5–8	Over 8
Average size, ha.	1·4	2·5	4·0	6·5	11·7
Labour force[a]	2·68	3·02	3·40	3·53	3·87
Do. excluding non-farm labour[b]	2·34	2·74	3·17	3·31	3·71
Labour units per sq. km.	167	110	79	51	32
Average product per man-year tons grain equivalent[c]	1·49	1·75	2·06	2·44	2·97
Marginal per man-year tons grain equivalent[c]		1·0	0·94	1·41	1·56

[a] Computed from total number of persons on holding assuming, per 100 total population, 40 male labour units + 24 female, equivalent to 57 male labour units in all.

[b] Non-farm labour deduced from non-farm earnings, assuming that the average non-farm rate of pay was 200,000 dinars per man-year.

[c] Net farm income before tax converted on 32,000 dinars = 1 ton wheat.

Assumed number of man-hours per year, 2,000.

The first two diagrams measure not only the average product but also the marginal, that is to say, the additional grain equivalent obtained when an additional man-hour of labour is applied to the same land. For Gambia these show a nearly horizontal relationship (marginal product about the same as average product) up to a labour input of some 700 man-hours per ha. — after which the marginal product falls rapidly. The author's experience in the village showed that cultivators did in fact stop putting any further labour into cultivation at about this point. The Gambian male cultivator may not be able to read or write, but he knows the difference between marginal and average product, which is more than can be said for some highly educated accountants. In any

CHART IV.

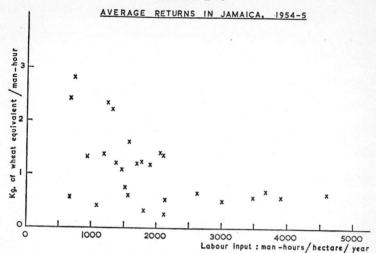

AVERAGE RETURNS IN JAMAICA, 1954-5

case, since available lands were not scarce, we should, on the whole, expect marginal product to be similar to average.

In Jamaica[1] Edwards records that the average investment of labour to land was high, but that the average productivity of labour was low.

For India, a pioneering study comparing yields on farms with different levels of labour input was made near Agra by Shastri[2] in 1956. More recently the government of India has published a series of studies of varying quality in the economics of farm management in various States. Of all the States, the study[3] for Madras has been most thoroughly done, and contains estimates of marginal product. The following diagram compares Shastri's and the Madras State results.

Of the data obtained in the other States, the only available information on marginal product of labour appears to be for Ahmednagar,[4] where it was 0·34 kg. sorghum, or 0·24 kg. wheat

---

[1] D. Edwards, *An Economic Study of Small Farming in Jamaica*, 1961.

[2] C. P. Shastri, *Indian Journal of Agricultural Economics*, January–March 1958. Sugar cane assumed 11 per cent sugar content which is converted to wheat equivalent on FAO factor of 1·03 kg. sugar = 1 kg. wheat.

[3] Government of India, *Studies in the Economics of Farm Management*, Madras 1954–55, p. 134–7. Values expressed as rough rice on the local price of 0·284 rupees/kg., and then converted to wheat by FAO factor of 0·8 kg. rough rice = 1 kg. wheat. Assumed 8-hour day.

[4] Government of India, *Studies in the Economics of Farm Management*, Bombay 1954–5.

G

equivalent/man-hour (assuming a 10-hour day). In many of the tables given, it was not possible to distinguish the effects of increasing inputs of labour and of bullock power. The average product of wheat on irrigated land near Agra is a little over 1 kg./man-hour. Rather surprisingly, at the lowest levels of labour input

CHART V.

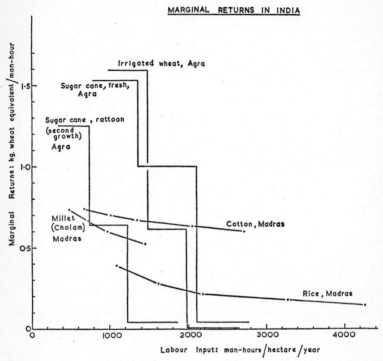

(below 1500 man-hours/ha./year) marginal product is higher than average, i.e. the labour input has been inadequate. Marginal product however falls rapidly nearly to zero with higher labour inputs. Marginal product of sugar cane, measured at world prices, also falls off similarly — though this effect has been masked by the high price for sugar, relative to world prices, paid by the Indian government (which has led now to India's producing more sugar than she can consume).

In the Madras area the average wage of men works out at about ·335 kg. wheat equivalent/man-hour, of women ·18. The men's wage is below the marginal returns from cotton and millet, but not from rice. The proceeds from the sales of the two former crops would therefore seem to contain a considerable rent element.

That there is a large land-rent element in the proceeds of Indian agriculture can be inferred from some carefully compiled results[1] in which, as an economic experiment, four comparable holdings of 2 ha. each were leased to farmers on condition that they kept accurate accounts. Over the period 1950–4 the average expenditure on labour for each holding was 687 rupees/year, of which 221 Rs. was for hired labour and the remainder for family labour computed at the hiring rates (1·56 Rs./day for men, 1·07 for women, and 0·62 for boys). The net proceeds for the average farm, after debiting the above payments for labour, after debiting interest on equipment and working capital at 12 per cent per annum, and after debiting a nominal land tax (30 Rs.), but before debiting rent on the land, was as much as 1759 Rs., or 2½ times the earnings of labour, computed at the current wage rates.

Through the use of chemical fertilizers, good cultivation methods, and many years of diligent plant breeding, rice yields in Japan are far higher than in other Asian countries. But there appears to be a maximum economic labour input per ha. The Japanese Ministry of Agriculture publish rice yields and labour inputs for the 46 prefectures (administrative regions) of Japan. There is no discernible statistical relation between these two. Labour inputs range from 1400 to 2500 man-hours (including female labour)/ha./year, all of them apparently above the economic limit. This result suggests the conclusion that above this limit additional labour inputs yield, in general, no return.

Maruta[2] made a mathematical analysis of the accounts of 30 poor farms in Kagoshima province which had, he pointed out, the highest proportion of population engaged in agriculture and the lowest per head agricultural income of all provinces in Japan, despite its favourable climate, which permits the growing of oranges and tea. Average labour input was as high as 2700 man-hours/ha./year. Maruta's equation showed that the output obtained was almost entirely explainable in terms of the inputs of land and capital. The marginal product of labour appeared to be only 50 yen/day, or 0·075 kg. wheat equivalent/man-hour (the farm price of brown, or partially milled rice, whose value on the FAO scale is precisely equivalent to that of wheat, was 67 yen/kg.).

[1] Institute of Agriculture, Anand, Bulletin No. 4, March 1958.
[2] S. Maruta, *Memoirs of the Faculty of Agriculture*, Kagoshima University No. 1, 1956.

In a later study (December 1958), more refined, Maruta obtained higher figures for marginal productivity, though still very low. Distinguishing hired and family labour, he obtained marginal products of 61 and 15 yen/hour respectively. Tutiya[1] estimated marginal products at only 11 yen/hour for rice, inappreciable for wheat, barley and oranges, but at 29 for tea and 34 for sweet potato. These two latter were above the current wage level, i.e. it was worth while hiring labour to produce them.

A survey in Thailand[2] showed farms with a range of labour inputs approximately from 500 to 2000 man-hours/ha./year (assuming a 1300-hour year). The average yield was about 2·2 tons of rough rice/ha., and no discernible variation with labour input could be seen.

Zero marginal output can occur in Communist agricultural economics too. A number of medium-yielding cotton farms in Uzbekistan in 1953[3] showed no change in yield as the labour input rose from 233 to 348 man-days/ha. (extremely high labour inputs in any case, even for cotton).

A most interesting new approach to the problem of marginal productivity in rice growing was Sarkar's study for Ceylon.[4] Comparing different districts in Ceylon, he obtained the equation:

Log(yield of rough rice in bushels) = ·0802 log(area in acres) + ·5570 log(labour input in man-days of 8 hours, women counting half men) + ·2453 log(all other costs, measured in Rs.) − 0·0141

(1 bushel rough rice = 20·5 kg.; wheat equivalent of rough rice = 0·8)

To calibrate his equation he then assumes (which does not appear to be quite the case) that the marginal product can be equated to the subsistence wage paid in the agricultural districts, which at that time was 1·9 Rs. per day (equivalent to 3·9 kg. of rough rice). Taking 268 days as a normal year, he then deduces that 28 per cent of the agricultural population is surplus. An interesting feature of this result is that the extent of surplus labour appears to be almost unrelated to the size of holding.

[1] K. Tutiya, *Quarterly Journal of Agricultural Economics*, No. 1, 1955. In Japanese.
[2] J. W. Mellor and R. D. Stevens, *Journal of Farm Economics*, 1956, p. 780.
[3] *Economic Bulletin for Europe*, November 1957, p. 60.
[4] N. K. Sarkar, 'A method of estimating surplus labour in peasant agriculture in overpopulated underdeveloped countries', *Journal of the Royal Statistical Society*, Series A, Vol. CXX, 1957.

Taking Sarkar's equation, for a given area of land, and with miscellaneous expenditure also being given, we can rewrite it:

Log(number of labour days) = constant − log(marginal productivity of labour measured in bushels per year)/0·443

So, if we raise the number of labour days by the factor of 1/0·72 (i.e. raising it from Sarkar's computed to its actual level) the left-hand side of the equation is raised by 0·145, so marginal productivity of labour is lowered by the antilog of ·064, i.e. 16 per cent. In this way we deduce the true marginal productivity of labour at 0·41 kg. rough rice/man-hour, as against the wage of 0·49.

The marginal productivity of land, that is to say the increase in output which can be obtained by increasing the amount of land cultivated, labour input being given, is a sort of reciprocal measure of the marginal productivity of labour. In Iraq, a comparatively advanced economy,[1] some calculations were made for a farm family of given size, if it were able to occupy holdings increasing progressively from 7·5 to 12·75 ha. Expressed in tons of wheat/ha. (the price of a ton of wheat was 20 Iraqi dinari) marginal productivity appeared to be actually increasing as the scale was ascended, beginning at 1 ton wheat equivalent/ha. and rising to 1·4.

Maruta found a marginal productivity of a hectare of land in mixed farming at about 0·6 tons of brown rice equivalent (equal to wheat equivalent); but for rice growing on irrigated land the figure was 1·2 tons for the larger farms with hired labour, and 4·1 tons (i.e. marginal productivity about equal to average) on the smaller farms without hired labour.

Bicanic's results for Yugoslavia[2] indicate a marginal return of almost exactly 1 ton of wheat/ha. for the smallest farms of 2 ha. or so, falling to 0·44 tons on the larger farms of about 8 ha. Throughout the range, it is interesting to see, the marginal return is a little less than half the average.

Finally we must consider the wages paid to agricultural labour, which should be equal to the marginal productivity of labour. We may open with a bold generalization by de Farcy.[3] Three kg. of cereals, he says, is the usual reward for a day's work in a subsistence economy, whether it be India now, Russia at the beginning

[1] Government of Iraq Development Board, *Diyala and Middle Tigris Projects*, Report No. 3, 1959. Estimates by Jewett, kindly supplied by Hunting Technical Services.

[2] International Association for Income and Wealth Conference, De Pietersberg, 1957.

[3] *Revue de l'Action Populaire*, April 1962.

of the present century, or France in the eighteenth century —
and among subsistence cultivators in Borneo, as we saw in Chapter
III.

We can test de Farcy's proposition for eighteenth-century France,
and the subsequent growth of wages.[1]

AGRICULTURAL WAGES IN FRANCE

Year	Man's wage Frs./day	Equivalent in kg. wheat/day
1700	0·5	2·6
1788	0·6	2·8
1813	1·05	3·5
1840	1·3	4·6
1852	1·42	6·1
1862	1·85	6·1
1872	2·0	6·5

From the same source we also have some information for
Belgium.

AGRICULTURAL WAGES IN BELGIUM

Year	Man's wage Frs./day	Equivalent in kg. wheat/day
1830	1·08	2·9
1840	1·14	3·0
1856	1·36	3·7
1874	2·04	6·6
1880	2·4	8·6

The Irish agricultural labourer's wage[2] of 8½d./day in 1836 was
equivalent to 3·4 kg. wheat, or 5 kg. barley. In the 1930s, rural day
wages in the Middle East appear to have averaged 8–10 kg. of
wheat. Spanish day wages have been worth 11 kg. of wheat/day
(at farm prices) both in the 1900s and now.[3]

Beckett's casual labourers in West Africa received the equivalent
of only 3·4 kg. of maize/day in the 1930s; regular workers, including the value of their food, housing and 'customary pickings'
(clandestine sale of some of the crop to itinerant buyers) earned
4½ kg. maize/day. Comparing these figures with those of farmer's
average incomes, we must conclude that marginal product was

---

[1] Data from: de Foville, *La France Economique*.
[2] A. L. Bowley, *Journal of the Royal Statistical Society*, 1899, p. 401.
[3] Vandellos, *Metron*, 1925, gives 2 pesetas a day for the average of 1903–12;
Fr. Garavilla, Burgos (private communication), gives 47 pesetas a day for the
present wage.

high relative to average product per unit of labour. Both farmers and labourers in West Africa at that time, however, were suffering from an extremely low price of cocoa, and relatively high price of maize, far above its price in East Africa. The average wage in Tanganyika, as recorded by Couchman[1] in the 1930s was the equivalent of 6 kg./day of maize or sorghum (0·4 shillings).

Wages in Guatemala,[2] on the other hand, averaged only 4·1 kg maize/day, while average product was 2·9 kg./hour. The reason for this great difference is hard to see — unless some sort of serfdom prevails. The wage labourer in Vietnam, Gourou reported, received in the 1930s 1 fr./day for a period which might vary from 120 to 200 days per year, and the equivalent of a steady 220 fr./year in kind. If we spread this latter remuneration over 200 days, his total remuneration is the equivalent of 2·4 kg./day of milled rice (equivalent to 2·85 kg. of wheat). For China, Buck quotes abundant wage data, but only in silver currency, which can be translated only into grain equivalents in an indirect manner. The day wage here however appears to average about $3\frac{1}{2}$ kg. of Buck's 'grain equivalent' (which includes a considerable proportion of coarser grains).

A pioneer of village surveys of subsistence cultivators was Gilbert Slater, Professor of Economics in the University of Madras, who surveyed a number of villages in southern India in 1916. Twenty years later they were resurveyed by the University.[3]

These surveys revealed the existence, in some villages, of workers who had become, in effect, serfs. The law of British India did not recognize serfdom, not indeed the attachment of sons for their fathers' debts, which seems to have been the way in which this quasi-serfdom arose, among poor people who were too uninformed or too frightened to seek legal redress. (Economic historians speculate that serfdom in Dark Age Europe may have originated in a similar manner.) This serfdom did, however, have the compensating advantage that the wage was paid regularly, whether work was available or not. As it came to be replaced by free contract and money payments, the workers earned money only on the days on which work was available, often as few as 100 per year in this part of India.

---

[1] Fuggles Couchman, *East African Journal of Agriculture*, March 1939.
[2] Higbee, *Geographical Review*, April 1947.
[3] University of Madras Economic Series, No. 1, *Some South Indian Villages*, ed. G. Slater, 1918; No. 4, *Some South Indian Villages*, A Resurvey, ed. P. J. Thomas, 1940.

TABLE XIX. EARNINGS OF LANDLESS LABOURERS IN SOUTHERN INDIA EXPRESSED IN KG. GRAIN EQUIVALENT

Village	Grain equivalent used	Yearly wage				Daily wage	
		1916	1925	1932	1936	1916	1936
Guruvayur, Malabar	Rough rice	657	561	545	682		
Watakancheri, Cochin	do.	663			663		
do. women					497		
do. boys					331		
Vunagatla, West Godavari[a]	do.						
Men		686			624–1664	2·6–3·4	5·2
Women		—				1·3–1·7	3·9–4·5
Boys		329				0·9–1·1	2·0–2·6
Vadamalaipuram, Ramnad	Millet						
Men					454	5·4	
Women						2·7	

[a] A prosperous village with an income from toddy-tapping, reduced to destitution since prohibition was introduced.

It appears that the situation changed little over twenty years, and that some of the earnings were extremely low. The village of Vadamalaipuram suffers from an extremely dry climate, and there is little work outside the 2½ months' monsoon period. Recently however a well has been installed, with an electric pump, making the growing of a variety of crops possible; and the women of the village have demanded a wage of 3½ kg. grain/day.

The average wage in 1954 in the Madras district, as shown by the official survey, was 3·35 kg. rough rice/day for a man.

The length of the average working day for a casual labourer in Asia (and in eighteenth- and nineteenth-century Europe) is usually regarded as 10 hours, in Africa less. Some of the wages reviewed suggest therefore a marginal productivity of only about 0·3 kg. grain equivalent/man-hour. This is compatible with the other information which we have obtained about the marginal productivity of labour engaged in subsistence agriculture in densely populated areas.

CHAPTER VI

Rents and Prices of Agricultural Land

Early in the nineteenth century, David Ricardo, a successful stockbroker-economist, developed the Ricardian Theory of Rent, which has been ever since a basic proposition in the teaching of economics. Rent was not, as had hitherto been supposed, an element in the cost of production — this might appear to be true for the individual farmer, but the rent of land was not a cost which should be taken into account in estimating in general the costs of producing a commodity. Rents were not a cause, but a consequence, of the differences between costs of production on different farms. Surveying the rather simple agricultural institutions of his day, Ricardo concluded that these arose largely from differences in the fertility of the soil, and in transport costs. As demand increased, farms of worsening fertility had to be brought into cultivation — we can still see traces of what was going on in England at that time in districts like Dartmoor, when the high prices of the Napoleonic Wars pushed the margin of cultivation up the slopes on to cold acid lands, which were soon afterwards abandoned again. These lands at the limit of cultivation, Ricardo taught, received no rent. Every other piece of farm land tended to receive a rent, equivalent to the difference between its costs of production and those of the land at the limit of cultivation.

Though we must now regard this theory as excessively simplified, it was nevertheless a permanent contribution to economic knowledge. It was not universally accepted in Ricardo's time. Ricardo taught other doctrines, including the unpleasing idea that the rate of population growth among the labouring classes was so great that competition between them was always bound to drive their wages down to the very minimum of subsistence. William Cobbett referred to Ricardo as 'nothing but a stupid bothering stockbroker, with a head full of discount, scrip, omnium, percentages and shades'.

The Ricardian theory of rent may be regarded as a preliminary statement of the more exact proposition, stated later in the nineteenth century by Jevons and Marshall, that we should expect rent

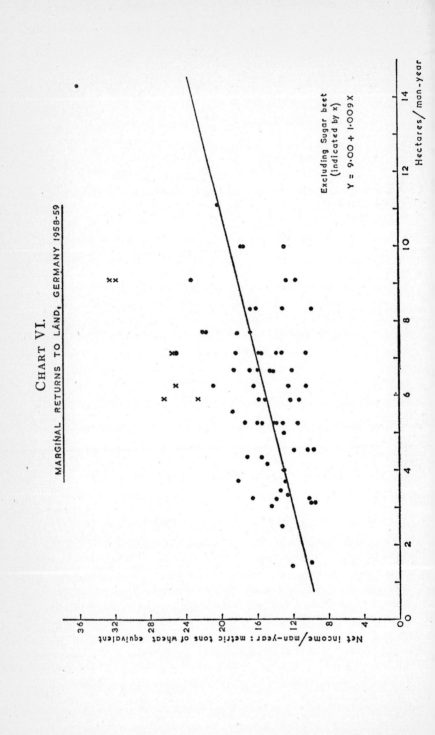

CHART VI.

MARGINAL RETURNS TO LÄND, GERMANY 1958-59

Excluding Sugar beet
(indicated by x)

Y = 9·00 + 1·009 X

Net income/man-year : metric tons of wheat equivalent

Hectares/man-year

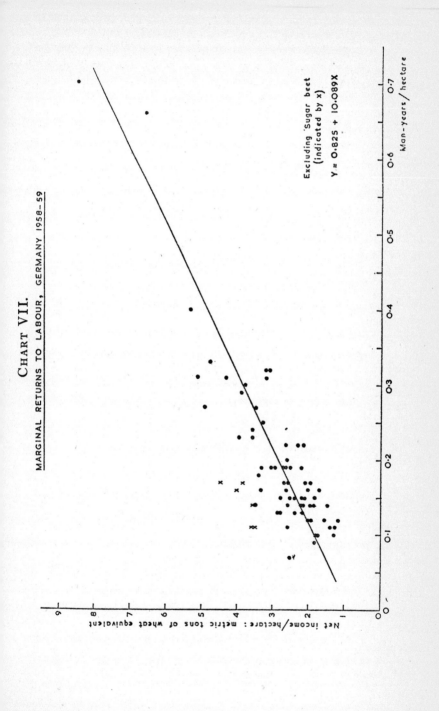

CHART VII.

MARGINAL RETURNS TO LABOUR, GERMANY 1958–59

Excluding 'Sugar beet
(indicated by x)

Y = 0·825 + 10·089X

Man-years/hectare

Net income/hectare : metric tons of wheat equivalent

to be determined by the marginal productivity of land. This latter statement, in its turn, we may expect to see supplanted eventually by the use of production functions. Without formally drawing production functions we can well gauge the nature of the relationship from data for German family farms[1] in 1958–9. The fitted line showing returns to labour (excluding sugar beet which is a favoured crop with limited output) indicates a marginal productivity per man-year of labour of 10 tons wheat equivalent (4237 DM), which is comparable with the average German rural wage of 4656 DM. The return to land indicates a marginal productivity per ha. of 1 ton wheat equivalent (424 DM); if the marginal return to land is of this order, present land prices up to 10,000 DM/ha. are fully understandable. Even at 10,000 DM the price is only a 24 years' purchase of rent.

At present (although a more elaborate function may later be found necessary) the Cobb-Douglas function is the one generally used. This may be formulated as follows:

Let P be production, L the input of labour, A the area of land used.

$$\text{Then } P = L^a A^b$$

Even in the most primitive agriculture, however, it is not entirely true to say that land and labour are the sole factors of production. In the more advanced forms of agriculture, there will be very large inputs of equipment, fertilizers, and other commodities. It may be convenient for some purposes, therefore, to define P not as the gross product, but as the 'factor income' of agriculture, after debiting the cost of all these other inputs. In the simpler forms of agriculture, it is permissible to assume that expenditure on these inputs bears a small and fairly constant relation to the gross product; not so however in the advanced forms of agriculture.

A simple differentiation of the Cobb-Douglas function shows that a measures the marginal productivity of labour, b of land, as a proportion of the total product, if we assume that there are no general economies or dis-economies of scale, which is equivalent to assuming that $a+b=1$, which is found to be approximately the case. According to the way in which P has been defined, therefore, b represents the proportion which the rent of land may be expected to bear either to the gross product or to the total factor income, according to the way in which the equation has been constructed.

[1] H. Priebe, *Neuzeitliche Familienbetriebe*, Heft 1, Forschungsstelle für bäuerliche Familienwirtschaft e. V., Frankfurt am Main, 1961.

A great deal of further research on this subject is needed, but there are some preliminary indications, at any rate for low-income agriculture, that the order of magnitude of b may be about $\frac{1}{2}$. In Nigeria[1] Cobb-Douglas functions were prepared showing a co-efficient for land of 0·6 in the case of cocoa and 0·5 in the case of food crops. From the data given in the previous chapter, we conclude that marginal product of labour may sometimes be considerably less than half average product in India, is about half in Iraq, is almost nominal in Japan, and is rather over half in Yugoslavia.

It appears to follow, therefore, that in the case of low-income agriculture generally, rent may be expected to take nearly half of the gross product. A number of instances can indeed be found in which this has occurred. But the proposition is subject to certain very important qualifications, which will be discussed below.

Ricardo, having in mind no doubt what we would now call a very simplified model, conveyed the idea of rents being highest on the high-yielding land and low, coming down to zero, on the low-yielding land.[2] An important qualification to this simple principle was pointed out in the 1880s by the French economist Leroy-Beaulieu, whose work received little attention from his contemporaries — perhaps because he wrote in a language which was understood by ordinary men. Comparing (his figures are given in the large table following) rents in the highest yielding region of France (Departement Nord) and in the lowest yielding mountain regions, he showed that, while the absolute amount of rent was higher in the former, yet the proportion of the product taken by rent was higher in the poorer regions. For the marginal productivity of the land to represent half or any other specified proportion of the total product does not in itself suffice to bring rents up to that proportion of the total product. A further necessary condition is that, in respect of any area of land under consideration, the intending tenants should, as we might put it, have nowhere else to go; that is to say, that there is no great competition for their labour either from more fortunately situated agricultural lands, or from industry.

This principle could not be better illustrated than by figures of

---

[1] Galletti, Baldwin and Dina, *Nigerian Cocoa Farmers*, 1955, pp. 314 and 328.

[2] There is a Cambridge legend concerning Fay, Marshall's disciple, travelling in northern Canada and, on reaching the furthermost point of agricultural settlement, promptly sending a postcard to Marshall to say that he had at last found the marginal farm.

CHART VIII.

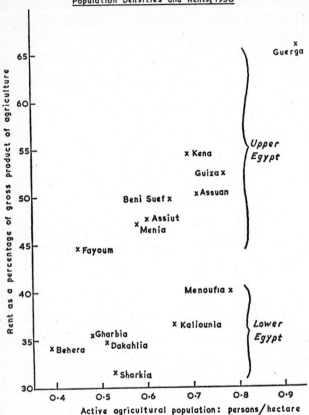

rents in the different provinces of Egypt in 1950. (This indeed was
almost the last year of that unfettered renting of Egyptian agricultural land, before the land reforms, which we need to illustrate our
principle.) The proportion of the produce paid in rent is very
clearly seen to be a function of the density of agricultural population. The two quite different levels of the functions in Upper Egypt
and in Lower Egypt are the consequence of the greater accessibility, for the inhabitants of Lower Egypt, of industrial employment
in Cairo and Alexandria. The exception which proves the rule,
namely the province of Sharkia, where rents were lower than was
to be expected from the population density, even for Lower Egypt,

CHART IX.

<u>ITALY</u>
Interprovincial Comparison of Rents of Agricultural
Land and of Agricultural Population Density

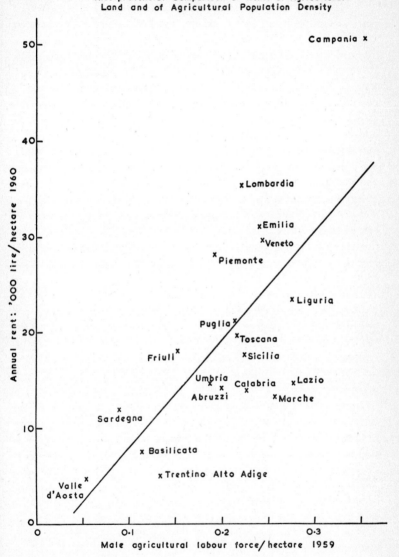

is explained by the fact that this province contained (at that time) a large British military base, offering abundant alternative employment.

We can see a similar relationship between rents and agricultural population density in Italy;[1] except that in this case it appears that the rise in rents even accelerates, as we come to the provinces of highest rural population density. The proximity of Rome apparently brings down rents in Lazio. The province of Trentino-Alto Adige contains a great deal of mountain land. Marche is peculiar in that very little land is leased, except marginal strips to enlarge existing farms. It is interesting to see that two of the poorest provinces, Sardinia and Basilicata, are sparsely populated and low rented (though allowance must be made for their containing a proportion of mountain land, some of which is in communal ownership, and leased for grazing).

For the whole of Italy (unlike many other countries) land prices and rents have been slowly falling, as more alternative employment becomes available.

It is very interesting to trace the same principle historically. Herlihy's figures (see main table) for early mediaeval Italy show rents fixed at a low proportion of the produce; he has abundant evidence of landowners competing with one another to attract tenants. 'Let leases be given only for one-quarter of the grain and one-third of the wine' was the standard of fairness decreed by the Church authorities, meeting at Cremona in 1066. By the twelfth century, population density in the rural areas had reached a saturation level, in relation to the conditions of the time, and rents rose sharply.

In the more spacious land of France, on the other hand, even the high rate of population growth in the thirteenth century (some historians believe that the population of France in the early fourteenth century was as high as 30 million) did not bring the proportion of the product paid in rent above some 14 per cent. The subsequent decline in rents indeed itself may be taken as an indication of the fall in population in the period of the Hundred Years War and the Great Plagues, even if we did not have independent evidence for it. The proportion of the product taken by rent was rising rapidly in the later eighteenth century — a fact of which political historians should have taken more account, in helping to

---

[1] The authors are very grateful to Benedetto Barberi, Director General of the Italian Istituto Centrale di Statistica, for information and advice on this subject.

explain the Revolution of 1789. Ancient Greece also shows a very low proportion paid in rent.

In England, on the other hand, it appears that saturation density in the rural areas had already been reached by the late seventeenth century — there is evidence, in the writings of Gregory King and elsewhere, of the existence of substantial rural 'disguised unemployment' at that time; a high ratio of rent to total agricultural factor income prevailed until late in the nineteenth century, when industrial employment and emigration overseas were finally to bring it down.

In Malaya and Philippines we see rent taking a high proportion of product, in spite of their being sparsely populated countries, with much unused land. This unused land is thick jungle; besides being difficult to clear, there may be customary or legal restrictions upon its exploitation.

When taxes, rates, tithes and similar charges are imposed upon land as such (as opposed to taxes falling on all income or property), we should where possible measure rents *inclusive* of such charges. Economic analysis shows clearly that the incidence of such charges is upon the economic rent, i.e. actual rent plus tax equals economic rent.

The price of agricultural land is a consequence of its rent (less tax). This simple principle has proved very difficult of comprehension by landowners and farmers, who understandably say to themselves that they have paid so much for a piece of land, that they want a reasonable return on their outlay and that therefore rent is a consequence of price. But in addition, many land administrators and agricultural politicians have failed to grasp the economic principle that land prices are a consequence of rents, not *vice versa*. Some indeed have even gone so far as to talk about a supposed 'intrinsic' value of land.

This principle has been demonstrated by Rasmussen[1] using, not aggregates, but accurately kept accounts and records for a large number of individual farms co-operating under the Danish Farm Union. The data covered the period 1925 to 1950. Rasmussen examined all the recorded and estimated changes of the selling value of farms, and found that these changes correlated well with the variable (net income from farm/price of farm at beginning of period). The equation indicated, however, that an annual net return of only 2·7 per cent on the market value of the farm was the

[1] Results in course of publication, privately communicated.

point of equilibrium which kept the price of the farms stable. If the net return exceeded 2·7 per cent, buyers would begin to bid up the price of the farm.

The average rate of return on commercial investments in Denmark throughout this period was far higher. We are compelled to conclude therefore that the difference between these two returns must represent the advantages of land ownership other than the direct monetary return from farming in Denmark — the feeling of personal security, the sporting rights, the social position, possibly some taxation advantage. In a country like Britain, the social position and the sporting rights of land ownership count for a good deal more, and in addition there are very substantial death-duty concessions on agricultural estates; we should expect, therefore, the rate of return on agricultural land to be even lower than in Denmark, possibly approaching 1 per cent per annum only.

But hardly anybody seems to understand the position, judging from the persistency of the complaints, from so many countries, that landowners are not getting a fair return on their investment.

On the other hand, we must not assume that these non-monetary advantages of land ownership are constant at all times; nor that the ratio of the price of land to its rent is independent of commercial rates of interest. In some countries, the non-monetary advantages of holding land are small. At a given level of rent, moreover, and with the non-monetary advantages also given, the price of land will depend, not only upon changes in the rate of interest, but also upon the political outlook. Where landowners feel that their political future is quite secure, they may bid land up to very high prices; and conversely.

Converting all land prices into an equivalent in tons of wheat per ha., so as to make possible comparisons between very varied countries and times, the high figures shown at certain dates for Egypt, Japan and Belgium must be considered as an indication of this feeling of political security on the part of landowners, together with, of course, a high rural population density, and high rents of land.

Landowners can feel political stability in communist Yugoslavia where private ownership of small farms is permitted, and the price of land in the most densely populated region is about as high as anywhere in the world.

The rise in the price of agricultural land in the United States during the past decade probably represents a shrewd assessment of the increasing political security which American farmers now feel in their ability to go on extracting support from the U.S. Treasury.

In sparsely populated, newly settled countries, on the other hand, such as Brazil, the prices of land measured in real terms are low, and may indeed show a tendency to fall.

The comparatively low prices of land in pre-communist China probably measure the effect of political insecurity, largely counteracting the effects of high rural population density and lack of alternative employment, which would have been expected to raise prices. The nineteenth-century prices of land in the area devastated by the Taiping Rebellion provide probably the most striking example ever known of the effects of depopulation on land values.

The gradual upward trend of land values in India, with increasing population density, is of interest. In Japan, land values appear to have reached their maximum in the 1920s, and now to be falling, as more industrial employment becomes available.

TABLE XX.
RENTS AND PRICES OF AGRICULTURAL LAND

Country or Region	Date	Currency unit	Rent as % of		Rent/ha. land in		Price/ha. land in	
			gross product	factor income	money	tons grain equiv.	money	tons grain equiv.
RICA								
ypt	1st c. A.D.		34			0·64		
	4th c. A.D.		21			0·40		
	1877	£E			7·5	0·75	125	12·5
	1895	£E	31		3·3	0·52		
	1935–9	£E		53	17·1	1·82		
	1947–8	£E			42·5	1·99	1062	47·2
	1951	£E		35	59·5	2·79		
	1953	£E	32	45	49·4	2·31		
ana	1957		25–33			0·6–0·7		
MERICA								
azil:								
Matto Grosso 1st cl. land	1935	$US					5	0·2
" " " " 2nd cl. land	1948	$US					45	0·75
ao Paulo	1948	$US					30	0·5
le	1944	$US						
	1960		44		5	0·2		
atemala: sheep land	1947	$US	10			0·5–0·7		10·0
potato land	1947	$US	10	7				
aica	1959	£					86	3·5
A								
na:								
aiping War Area	1850	$C					480	16·3
	1860	$C					12	0·3
hinese Turkestan	1940		50–80				28	1·0
ing Hsien wheat region:								
dry	1928	$C	35–40		65		645	5·7
irrigated	1928	$C	35–40		116		1160	10·3
verage: wheat	1933		32			0·35		4·4
rice	1933		32			0·8		10·0
ia:								
unjab	1885	Rupee					74	1·4
	1900	Rupee					190	2·2
	1910	Rupee					306	3·5
	1916	Rupee					560	5·1

Country or Region	Date	Currency unit	Rent as % of		Rent/ha. land in		Price/ha. land in	
			gross product	factor income	money	tons grain equiv.	money	tons grain equiv.
Deccan	1914	Rupee					198	2·03
	1921–9	Rupee					277	1·75
	1930–9	Rupee					347	4·16
	1949–52	Rupee					830	2·35
All	1950	Rupee					1420	4·1
Median of districts	1957–8	Rupee					1635	3·6
Lowest — Rajasthan	1957–8	Rupee					250	0·6
Highest — Kerala	1957–8	Rupee					4700	10·5
Maharashtra — Bombay State	1940	Rupee			69	0·70	1085	11·1
Maharashtra — Bombay State	1954–6	Rupee		67	870	2·27	3710	9·7
Iraq: Northern	1930–40			25				
Southern	1930–40			70–80				
Israel	1933	Pruta		43				
Japan:	1873	Yen	50–60				407	20·3
Upland (non-irrigated)	1886	Yen					123	3·9
	1895	Yen					280	3·6
	1914	Yen				0·45	1480	10·6
	1930	Yen			78	0·50		
	1933	Yen				0·66		
	1938	Yen				0·75	3040	13·6
Irrigated rice land	1886	Yen					404	12·8
	1895	Yen					870	11·1
	1908	Yen					1820	18·0
	1914	Yen	38			0·86	2770	20·0
Japan	1919–21	Yen	51			0·88		
	1924–6	Yen					5600	22·1
	1927	Yen	47		311	1·49	6200	31·0
	1930	Yen			281	1·82		
	1933	Yen				0·79		
	1936	Yen	46		312	1·25	4200	21·0
	1938	Yen			316	1·40	5190	23·1
Rice land, Shiga Prefecture	1961	000 yen					2410	31·3
Malaya	1958	$M	50		173	0·82		
Syria: irrigated	1930–40	£S	60		325			
non-irrigated	1930–40	£S	40–50		55–70			
Philippines	1955	Peso		55	368	1·08	2934	8·6
EUROPE								
Belgium: arable land	1830	Fr.			57	0·16		
	1846	Fr.					2630	8·3
	1866	Fr.			108	0·43		
	1880	Fr.					4250	16·5
France:								
arable land	9th c.	Fr.					70	
	12th c.	Fr.	8				93	
wheat land			6–14					
olive land			9–25					
	1200–25	Fr.					135	
	1276–1300	Fr.					261	
	1301–25	Fr.	14		8	0·094	222	
	1325–50	Fr.	14					0·8
	1351–1400	Fr.	10			0·069	90	0·8
	1426–50	Fr.					68	
	1451–75	Fr.	10			0·064	48	
	1476–1500	Fr.	10			0·064	97	1·18
	1501–24	Fr.					95	1·49
	1576–1600	Fr.			17		317	
	1600–50	Fr.	10			0·065	292	1·22
	1650–1700	Fr.	13			0·085	428	2·25
	1700–50	Fr.	11		11	0·072	305	
	1788	Fr.	39	43	22·5	0·125	640	3·54
	1815	Fr.	45		35	0·134		
	1845	Fr.	26	33	31	0·103		
	1851	Fr.					1497	7·7
	1879	Fr.					2197	7·8
	1885	Fr.		41	73	0·32		
	1890	Fr.					1500	6·0
national average	1885	Fr.	18		50	0·225		
Dept. Nord — highest	1885	Fr.	15			0·45		
Dept. Cantal, Aveyron — lowest	1885	Fr.	31			0·195		

Country or Region	Date	Currency unit	Rent as % of		Rent/ha. land in		Price/ha. land in	
			gross product	factor income	money	tons grain equiv.	money	tons grain equiv.
rmany	1861	DM					525	2·3
	1889	DM					1500	7·7
eece	5th c. B.C.		8			0·075		
land	1884	£		19	1·36	0·18		
y: North and central	8th–11th c.		15					
All	12th c.		40					
	1930–9		26	35				
	1960	ooo lire			22·5	0·32	475	6·8
Campania: highest-priced land								
Basilicata: lowest do.		ooo lire			50·5	0·72	816	11·6
umania:		ooo lire			7·8	0·11	164	2·3
	1886	lei					33	0·13
owland	1905	lei					535	3·4
arable	1911–16	lei				0·02	988	5·5
	1929	ooo lei				0·03	32	0·9
	1932	ooo lei					16	
ain: dry land	1960	peseta					8000	1·9
irrigated land	1960						40000	9·5
ited Kingdom:								
and and buildings	1688	£		43				7·
goslavia:	1938	ooo din.						
lovenia	1938	ooo din.					25	25
oivodina	1954	ooo din.					7	7
erbia: densely settled areas	1954	ooo din.				0·4	150	7·5
ll	1957	ooo din.					450	22·5
lovenia	1957	ooo din.					166	4·8
							70	2·0

Sources and Notes to Table Rents on and Prices of Agricultural Land

EGYPT: Early centuries and 1895: D'Avenel, *La Richesse Privée depuis Sept Siècles*. Hectolitre taken as 75 kg. Yield in ancient world as estimated by Mitchell, *The Economics of Ancient Greece*.

1877: Baer, *A History of Landownership in Modern Egypt*.

Taxes took half the produce on medium- or low-quality land, the proportion having been raised from one-third in 1864 (except for a few favoured large landowners, whose tax was only £1·25/ha.). Baer agrees with Issawi that Egypt, at this time, was underpopulated rather than overpopulated — he records that taxation and fears of forced labour were causing land to be abandoned.

1935–9 and 1951: C. Issawi, *Egypt at Mid-Century*.

1947–8 and 1953: D. Warriner, *Land Reform and Development in the Middle East*.

1930s: Bresciani-Turroni, *Weltwirtschaftliches Archiv*, October 1933, estimates rent at only 38 per cent of factor income; Bonné, *Economic Development of the Middle East*, at 44 per cent. The latter considers that it had fallen to 42 per cent by 1950, *International Symposium on Desert Research*, Jerusalem, 1952.

GHANA: Dr. Torto, Deputy Director of Agriculture, private communication. Maize growing on worn-out cocoa land, cropped twice a year.

BRAZIL: Waibol, *Geographical Review*, October 1948; *Foreign Agriculture*, U.S. Department of Agriculture, June 1945, for Sao Paulo.

CHILE: Professor T. Davis, Cornell University, private communication.

GUATEMALA: Higbee, *Geographical Review*, April 1947.

JAMAICA: Edwards, *An Economic Study of Small Farming in Jamaica*.

CHINA: 1850 and 1860: Richtofen, quoted in Ping-ti Ho, *Studies in the*

Population of China, 1368–1953, Harvard University Press. Grain prices were not available for this period. In the eighteenth century Chinese prices were rising steadily, but at the end of the century rose only to 10 silver dollars (7·2 oz. silver)/ton, much below European prices of that time. It is assumed that Chinese prices went on rising with the impact of world trade, and that in 1850 and 1860 they stood at two-thirds of prices in U.S. which at that time also used a dollar based on silver (i.e. $44/ton in 1850, $53/ton in 1860).

Chinese Turkestan: Chang Chih-yi, *Geographical Review*, 1939. In this case the landowner provides water and draught animals as well as land.

Gamble, *Ting Hsien*, Institute of Pacific Relations.

Shen-pao Nien-Chien, *Year Book*, Shanghai, 1933, gives rents and land prices in relation to yields. FAO figures of average yield used (rice expressed rough).

Very much lower prices are quoted by Buck, *Land Utilization in China*, p. 37. It appears that he is quoting some official value of the land rather than its real selling price.

INDIA: Punjab: Calvert, *Indian Journal of Agricultural Economics*, December 1918, prices of cultivated land. Wheat prices from Brij Narain, *Indian Economic Life*, p. 105.

Deccan: 'Diskalkar, Resurvey of a Deccan Village', *Indian Society of Agricultural Economics*, 1960.

All India: Datta and Pratash, *Conference on Research in National Income*, New Delhi, 1957.

The Reserve Bank of India's *Rural Credit Follow-up Survey; 1957-8*, gives data of land values in 1957–8 per farm, from which land values per ha. can be computed for 12 districts, scattered throughout India.

Maharashtra data from Ghate and Patel, *Indian Journal of Economics*, 1942–3; and Institute of Agriculture, Anand, Bulletin No. 4, March 1958. Rent of land computed here as residual after imputing standard wages to family workers. Further data for villages in southern India, showing great variations between villages, were published by University of Madras in *Some South Indian Villages — a Resurvey*.

		Annual Rent		Land Price	
		1916	1936	1916	1936
		tons rough rice/ha.			
Watakancheri				4·2	3·3
Guruvayur	—outlying land			4·2	9·1
	village land		·91	6·1	12·1
Gangaikondan	—irrigated			38·2	43·4
	dry			6·0	7·3
Palakkurichi		·82	1·57		
Vadamalaipuram	—irrigated			13·9	8·8
	dry		·20	2·3	1·0
	do. with wells		·38		
Vunagatla	—black soil		·52		16·9
	—sandy soil		·36		9·1

Irrigated land is exceptionally scarce in Gangaikondan. Palakkurichi has exceptionally high yields. The higher price paid for land within the village of Guruvayur as compared with outlying land is said to be due predominantly to the agricultural value of the animal and human manure accumulating in the inhabited region.

IRAQ: D. Warriner, *Land and Poverty in the Middle East*, inclusive of taxes, 10 per cent in south Iraq.

ISRAEL: Bonné, *Archiv für Sozialwissenschaft*, 1933.

JAPAN: For 1873, *Journal of Economic History*, 1947. Included in the rents are: national land tax of 12·2 yen/ha. plus local tax of 4·1, or 16·3 yen in all, payable by the landowners, which represented 34 per cent of average gross production of rice land/ha., which was 2·4 tons, valued at 48 yen, measured apparently as brown rice of 80 per cent extraction. These taxes represented, see Dore, *Land Reform in Japan*, 4 per cent of the land value then assessed, giving 407 yen/ha. as the average assessment. In 1878 national and local taxes were reduced to 2½ per cent and ½ per cent of the assessed value respectively. The surveyed and assessed area was incomplete however, sometimes to the extent of 20 per cent.

Other land price data from Kurt Singer, *Economic Record*, Australia, December 1947. D'Avenel, *La Richesse Privée depuis Sept Siècles*, for 1895. *Industrial Bank Index* for 1908, and for rice prices from that date and for rents in 1919–21 and 1936; on double-cropped land an additional 4 per cent of gross product went to rent in each case, quoted Dore, *Land Reform in Japan*. Sale, *Journal of the Royal Statistical Society*, April 1911, for early rice prices. Rent in 1914 from Grajdanzex, *Institute of Pacific Relations*, November 1941. Yagi, *Kyoto University Economic Review*, 1930, p. 101 for 1927; Shiomi, *Kyoto University Economic Review*, 1931, for 1930. Research Institute of Farm Accounting, Kyoto University, for 1961. Other land values quoted 000 yen/ha. were vegetable land in Osaka Prefecture 3050, mixed farm land Kinki Prefecture 2440, poultry farm land in Hyogo Prefecture 1910, dairy farm land in Kyoto Prefecture 526. An index number of real land values, Economic Research Institute of Economic Planning Agency, Economic Bulletin No. 9, shows a heavy fall in the inflation period, followed by recovery.

Index of Real Land Values, 1934–6 = 100

1950	1951	1952	1953	1954	1955	1956	1957
22	21	31	44	62	80	93	98

MALAYA: Wilson, *Economics of Paddy Production in Northern Malaya*, Malayan Department of Agriculture, 1958. Rents in milled rice.

PHILIPPINES: Central Experiment Station Bulletin No.1, 1957. Equivalents in milled rice. Figures refer to net rent — 80 per cent of gross rent, after certain seed harvesting and other customary charges have been met by the landowner — and refer to rice land only. In Mindanao and Cagayan, lower rainfall areas, average farm land prices fall to some 1·7 tons rice equivalent/ha. Taxes are only 20 pesos/ha./year.

SYRIA: D. Warriner, *Land and Poverty in the Middle East*. Landowner's share on irrigated land rises to 80 per cent when he provides draught animals and equipment.

BELGIUM: Combe, *Niveau de Vie et Progrès Technique*. Leroy-Beaulieu, *La Repartition des Richesses*, for 1830 and 1866.

FRANCE: D'Avenel, *La Richesse Privée depuis Sept Siècles*. Mayer, International Association for Research in Income and Wealth, Series III, p. 74, for 1788, 1845, 1885 factor incomes. Assumed cultivated area 40 m. ha. in 1788 and 1845, and 48 m. in 1885. Rent includes 100, 200 and 500 m. fr. respectively for taxes. Chaptel, quoted in *Salaire*, Vol. III, p. 95, for rent in 1815. Leroy-Beaulieu, *La Repartition des Richesses*, regional data for 1895.

GERMANY: Combe, *Niveau de Vie de Progrès Technique*.

GREECE: Michell, *The Economics of Ancient Greece*.

IRELAND: Giffen, *Economic Enquiries and Studies*.

ITALY: Herlihy, *Agricultural History*, April 1959. Informazione Svimez, Gasparini. *Annuario dell'Agricultura Italiana*, 1960, pp. 144, 146. Istituto Centrale di Statistica, private communication, provincial data on agricultural labour force.

ROUMANIA: Mitrany, *The Land and the Peasant in Roumania*. Manoilesco, *Weltwirtschaftliches Archiv*, July 1935, for 1932.

SPAIN: Fr. Garravilla, Burgos; private communication.

UNITED KINGDOM: Gregory King, *Political Observations*.

YUGOSLAVIA: Vinski, International Association for Research in Income and Wealth, 1957 Conference. Mihailović, World Population Conference. Starc, Private communication. Rent shown for Voivodina includes 0·2 tons/ha./year tax. The rate of tax has recently been doubled.

CHAPTER VII

Labour and Land

From the information assembled in Chapter V we now have some knowledge, though much less than we would wish, on the falling off of the marginal returns to further labour inputs on a given area. In some cases the curve of marginal return plunges downwards steeply, and we can estimate fairly precisely the maximum feasible labour input per hectare for a given crop.

We seek to proceed from this to answer the more general question, namely how much land does a given agricultural population need or, conversely, on a given area of land, at what level of population density can we say that the land is overpopulated in an agricultural sense?

This question, apparently simple, raises a number of difficult subordinate questions. We have seen in Chapter III how the land required to feed one person may be as high as 10 sq. km. for a primitive people living entirely by hunting and fishing; may fall to 10 ha. (100 ha. = 1 sq. km.) for the simplest neolithic-type cultivators and herdsmen; for shifting cultivators, including the land waiting and regrowing trees for a 12–20-year period, still only 5 ha. for each person may be required, or even less in some fertile areas. The actual amount of land cultivated in any one year, if we take the Iban as an example, may be only about one-third ha./year. When pressure of population finally forces the shifting cultivator to become a sedentary cultivator, fallow land will disappear, or will be greatly reduced, but the per person requirements of land actually cultivated will be increased. The sedentary cultivator in India, for example, has to do without those reserves of fertility in the soil which most African cultivators are still able to replenish through their shifting cultivation; the Indian in consequence gets considerably lower yields per ha. for most of the important crops.

So far however we have been considering communities whose aim was to produce their subsistence, with a small margin to spare, perhaps desiring to exchange to a very limited extent — the Hanunóo, for example, trading 10–15 per cent of their product. Once we introduce the consideration that a community can produce cash crops, and can sell them, the amount of the land which they require, and the amount of labour which they devote to agriculture, may be expected to be greatly increased.

We may, however, make the assumption, mistakenly, that once a community has discovered the opportunity of earning and spending cash, it will promptly seek to work all the hours that are physically possible, in order to earn more. In fact, as we shall see below, such communities have very definite ideas about the amount of leisure which they consider desirable or, to speak more precisely, the proportion of their time which they wish to devote to non-agricultural pursuits. We must remember that out of their total of non-agricultural hours they have to find time to make their clothes, build and repair their houses, perform numerous religious and civic duties, and many other tasks which we have performed for us, before they have time for what we would regard as leisure and rest.

It is, on the other hand, true that the nearer and more insistent the opportunities are for earning and spending cash, the more the cultivator is likely to revise his ideas about leisure, or the relative numbers of hours to be devoted to agricultural and non-agricultural pursuits. He may not only take less leisure, but also pay someone to build his house, and perform similar tasks, if industrial goods are readily available for sale at low prices, as in Japan, for example. Conversely, in the remoter parts of Africa where few industrial goods are available, and those that are at a high price after all the expenses of transport and distribution have been met, the cultivator still builds his own house, etc., and also appears to take abundant leisure.

After cash cropping has begun, and after we have taken account of varying leisure preferences, we must still take account of changing methods of agriculture. When the cultivator has some margin to spare over his most immediate requirements for food, and for other goods for which he exchanges part of his crop, he also finds (as we saw in Chapter IV) that he has enough cereals to provide part of the ration for draught animals. Use of draught animals increases the area which one man can cultivate in a given time. In certain monsoonal climates, where the period in which cultivation is possible is very short, as in northern (but not southern) India, the use of draught animals may indeed be a necessary condition without which agriculture would not be possible at all. The employment of draught animals further increases the required acreage, because part of their food has to come from fodder crops or grass, in addition to from cereals.

So far we have assumed that the draught animals pull only a simply designed plough and harrow. Later, as in America and Europe up to the 1920s, while animals still provided the power, nevertheless a great variety of improved implements were designed for them to draw, greatly increasing the area which one man could economically handle. The whole process culminated in the introduction of the tractor.

So, after the introduction of cash cropping, land requirements per man increase, for two separate reasons; firstly, the increasing proportion of the working year which each man is willing to devote to agriculture, and secondly the technical improvements, which increase the area which he can handle in a given time.

We must of course carefully distinguish this definition of the area 'required' by each man, as between the amount of land which he would like to have in order to earn an economic living, and the area 'required' to produce his subsistence.

With such figures in our mind, not constant, but changing slowly with decreasing leisure preference, and changing sometimes rapidly with technical improvements, we may then examine the amount of land actually available, and if it falls short of 'requirements' we may complain (legitimately, so long as the definition of the words is carefully borne in mind) of 'underemployment', or of 'rural overpopulation' — the two phrases are reciprocal ways of describing the same thing.

If such 'underemployment' is shown to exist, we may then go on to conclude that there is 'surplus labour' in agriculture which could, to the advantage of everybody, be removed from its present employment and put into industrial or other work. This may be done simply by administrative decree, as in China in 1958, the year of the 'Great Leap Forward', with disastrous consequences. In countries where people are free, a wage or similar incentive is necessary to attract people from agriculture to industry. The required cash inducement is greater than one thinks. Raj[1] has estimated that an unemployed Indian countryman will be maintained at subsistence level by his family at the cost of about $\frac{3}{4}$ rupee/day. To induce him to start work, even in his own village he will have to be offered a wage of 1–$1\frac{1}{2}$ rupees/day, according to

---

[1] K. N. Raj, Director of the Agricultural Economics Research Centre, University of Delhi; private communication.

region; to induce him to take work outside his own village he will have to be offered 2 rupees/day or more.

But in any case even if these difficulties can be overcome, the 'surplus labour' is often more apparent than real, for the reason that the agricultural labour requirements vary greatly with the season. This is most marked in a strongly monsoonal climate, where a substantial labour surplus for nine months of the year may be followed by overwork and really acute labour shortage for three months. With less violence than in the monsoonal areas, the same may also be true of many other types of climate. The seasonality of demand for labour can be smoothed out by skilful programming — witness Clayton's remarkable work in East Africa,[1] quoted below. Similar attempts at programming are now being made in England, for the large arable farms in East Anglia, where there is acute peak of demand for labour in the months of September and October. But in advanced countries there is no need to carry this process too far. The need for such programming is more urgent in countries where most of the population depends upon agriculture, where less interchange with other employments is possible. In countries where agriculture represents a comparatively small proportion of the labour force, it is more satisfactory to meet acute temporary peaks of demand for labour by drawing labour from outside the normal ranks of the industry, even though high wages have to be paid to attract it for a short period; this is the method by which harvesting labour is recruited in America and Australia.

Glyn-Jones's study[2] of the Dusun in Borneo, already referred to, brings out some of these points. Their production of irrigated rice for their own subsistence occupies some five or six months during the year. During the rest of the year they do a certain amount of rubber tapping for cash. Glyn-Jones pointed out that they still had, on the whole, the subsistence cultivator's outlook, because she observed that the better the land, the smaller the area the average family would cultivate. At the time when she studied them, however, they were just beginning to feel their need for more cash, or for surplus rice which could be used in exchange in much the same way as cash, in the first place to buy work animals and ploughs, and sometimes to pay additional labour for the harvest, or to rent additional land.

[1] E. S. Clayton, 'Economic and Technical Optima in Peasant Agriculture', *Journal of Agricultural Economics*, May 1961.

[2] M. Glyn-Jones, *The Dusun of the Penampang Plains in North Borneo*, Report to the Colonial Office, unpublished.

Economists have been grumbling about subsistence cultivators' preference for leisure, and finding it difficult to understand, ever since the days of the founder of economics, Sir William Petty (one of the authors recalls with satisfaction that he was a Fellow of Brasenose: with less satisfaction that he changed sides twice during the Civil War). Petty wrote in 1691,[1] regarding the Irish, 'What need have they to work, who can content themselves with *Potato's*, whereof the Labour of one Man can feed forty?' Petty's figure was approximately correct, and was confirmed by Arthur Young, regarding the ability of one man to produce 50 tons of potatoes per year (to feed 40 people at 8 lb./person/day); but Petty failed to observe that a substantial quantity of milk and oatmeal were also included in the Irish diet at that time.

As Gourou pointed out, the whole question of the African's preference (where enough land is available) for shifting rather than sedentary cultivation is really one of preference for leisure.

The whole issue has been strikingly illuminated in some work done by Mujumdar.[2] It is well known that most Indian farm families do not have enough land to keep them fully occupied. Mujumdar had the extremely original idea of visiting a large number of these families (in the Kanarese-speaking region of Bombay State, whose language he spoke) and asking how much land they would take if they were free to buy all that they wanted. He then translated this, plus the land which they already owned, into terms of man-hours/working member of the family/year, and got the surprising result shown in the diagram. In a country where all goods and labour are really held in common within the family, to an extent which we find hardly comprehensible, it follows that the families with the largest number of labour units are the richest, with the least number the poorest. (This goes a long way to explain the Indian desire for large numbers of offspring, sons for preference.)

In Bengal, where the soil and rainfall are very good, some of the land is double cropped, and the labour input per ha. very high. Nevertheless, Ghosh and Anukulchandra[3] found there, from a detailed study of land registers, that when the land held by any family exceeded 3 ha., they tended to let some of it to the neighbours. Unfortunately we do not have data about the size of family, or the average labour input per ha.; but however high (say 2000

---

[1] Sir William Petty, *Political Arithmetick*.
[2] Reserve Bank of India, private communication.
[3] Ghosh and Anukulchandra, 'Problems of Sub-Marginal Farming in West Bengal', *Indian Journal of Agricultural Economics*, Vol. V, No. 1, March 1950.

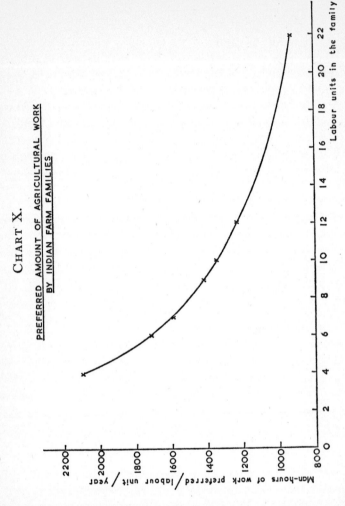

CHART X.

PREFERRED AMOUNT OF AGRICULTURAL WORK
BY INDIAN FARM FAMILIES

man-hours/ha./year) we assume the labour input and however low (say 5 workers) we assume the size of family, we are bound to conclude that the wealthier families prefer a short working year (1200 hours on the above assumptions). In some of the remoter parts of Africa we hear of men devoting less than 1000 hours/year to agricultural work. Baldwin[1] sampled two cocoa-farming villages in northwest Nigeria and found that the average number of working hours per adult working male per year were 997 and 1327 respectively.

[1] K. D. S. Baldwin, *The Niger Agricultural Project*, Blackwell, Oxford, 1957.

These represented 660 and 800 man-hours/ha./year, a level of labour input which for marginal productivity is still high. Anne Martin[1] found that in the comparatively economically advanced region of Calabar in Southern Nigeria men averaged throughout the year only 4 hours/day agricultural work. Platt[2] found in Nyasaland in 1938 that the average amount of land cultivated in three villages was only 1·1 ha./family. Hours/year ranged from 400–900 for men, 580–760 for women, and 67–80 for children.

One of the authors found[3] in Gambia in 1949 that adult men and women engaged in agriculture averaged only 855 hours/year (133 days) in agricultural work. In the village of Warwar in the Cameroons in 1953, a subsistence economy into which cash cropping was just being introduced, Refisch found[4] that for most of the year the men averaged 4, the women 5 hours/day agricultural work; but for some three months each year both sexes averaged 10 hours/day.

For the Toupourri tribe in North Cameroun, Guillard[5] gives labour days per year spent on other work as well as work in the fields.

	Average Number of Days Spent	
	Men	Women
Work in the fields	106	82
Other work	88	107
Free time	161	165
Sickness	10	11

One reason why African farmers do not produce more is that while they would like to buy more industrial goods, and would be willing to produce more crops in exchange for them, they are hampered by the lack of transport, and inadequate marketing organization. This is true of crops even with high value per unit of weight such as cocoa and coffee; and there is a limit to the amount of these crops which the farmer can grow. Good roads are Africa's

[1] A. Martin, *The Oil Palm Economy of the Ibibio Farmer*, Ibadan University Press, 1956.
[2] Platt, B. S., *Nutrition Survey*, Colonial Office Library (Mimeographed).
[3] M. R. Haswell, *Economics of Agriculture in a Savannah Village*, Colonial Research Studies No. 8, 1953; and privately communicated.
[4] University of London M.A. thesis in Anthropology (available in Colonial Office library).
[5] J. Guillard, 'Essai de mesure de l'activité du paysan africain: le Toupourri', *Agronomie Tropicale*, Vol. XIII, No. 4, Paris, July–August 1958.

real priority need: without them crops have lost a large part of their value by the time they are carried to market.

Among the primitive cultivators in Guatemala[1] Sol Tax found the average man working only 87 days/year, i.e. about 950 man-hours/ha./year on an average plot of 0·74 ha., to produce 2 tons of maize (2·1 kg./man-hour). In Jamaica[2] on the other hand small farmers are found to work a median of 2500 hours, even though they appear to have almost zero marginal productivity at this level of labour input (see also Chapter V).

The amount of labour which can be economically expended on a given area of land varies greatly both with the crops cultivated and the agricultural methods available. We have considered pre-dominantly so far the marginal returns, and the economic limits to labour expended on cereal cultivation, for the reason that this must be the primary concern of subsistence cultivators. A good deal more labour can be economically expended on a given area when growing cassava and other root crops. But we should not take this too much into account; if people depend upon these crops for more than a certain proportion of their diet, they will suffer from protein shortage. Some of the cash crops, such as cotton, and above all tobacco, can have very large amounts of labour expended upon them. But the production of these crops depends upon adequate access to markets, requires considerable skill, and in any case the farm communities which we are considering will still have to de-vote the main part of their energies to producing their subsistence requirements, and only a fraction of their land can be under commercial crops.

De Vries thought that the introduction of draught animals was not economically feasible until production had reached 500 kg. grain equivalent/person/year. (He did not consider the exception discussed above, namely monsoonal climates with a very short rainy season, where the use of draught animals may be unavoid-able, however poor the cultivator may be.) One of the facts which emerges is that the draught animals are as likely to suffer under-employment as the men. In the East Bengal Province of Pakistan, admittedly a very densely populated area, provincial agricultural officials[3] have estimated that draught oxen are capable of working

[1] S. Tax, *Penny Capitalism, a Guatemalan Indian Economy*, Smithsonian Institution of Social Anthropology, Publication No. 16, Washington, 1953.

[2] D. Edwards, *An Economic Study of Small Farming in Jamaica*, Institute of Social and Economic Research, Kingston, Jamaica, 1961.

[3] Private communication.

1200 hours/year, that there were about three times as many oxen in the Province as were actually required to do the work, and that much of the cultivation was done at a pace far slower than that of which the oxen were capable. Shastri[1] has estimated that the percentage of the capacity of the draught oxen utilized in India varies from 24 per cent on the smallest farms to 40 per cent on the largest. In the Punjab on the other hand, an area of comparatively large farms, the oxen are estimated to be employed for a full working year of 161 days (the animals working fewer hours each day than the man, as has always been the case).

A valuable pioneer study of underemployment in India was made by Tarlok Singh.[2] He devised an ingenious method of estimating the labour input required for a given amount of land in various areas, based on the numbers of ploughs and plough teams. We have seen above that nearly all the draught oxen in India work well below their theoretical capacity (although at the same time most of them are fed at a rate far below that required for doing a full year's work). Tarlok Singh, in effect, based his calculations on the assumption that the degree of underemployment of draught oxen would be fairly uniform. At any rate, his results for Bengal came out very close to those which Ghosh & Anukulchanbra calculated by quite a different method.

Tarlok Singh's estimates of actual as a percentage of full employment are compared with those published by the Agrarian Affairs Sub-Committee of the Congress Party in 1949 (treating 300 days as a full year's work). The data were computed from the 1941 Census, with the names of the Provinces as they were then, including a good deal of what is now Pakistan territory. The territories of what were then 'Indian States' have been omitted.

The two methods agree quite well for the most densely populated area, Bengal. (The Agrarian Reform Sub-Committee figure is on the assumption that both jute and rice are grown; if jute only is grown, the figure should be halved.) Agreement is also good for Bombay Province (now Maharashtra and Gujarat States), the most industrialized part of India, where we would expect that some of the rural underemployed would be drawn into industrial work. For Sind (now part of Pakistan) Tarlok Singh estimated that the labour supply was actually inadequate, and barely adequate for

[1] Economic Weekly, 29 October 1960.
[2] *Poverty and Social Change*, 1945. The author is now Secretary of the Indian Planning Commission.

I

TABLE XXI.   UNDEREMPLOYMENT IN INDIA

	Estimated Ha./Man required for Full Employment	Actual as Percentage of Full Employment	
	Tarlok Singh	Tarlok Singh	Congress Agrarian Reforms Sub-Committee
Bengal	2·8	58	60
United Provinces	3·2	59	59
Bihar	3·2	61 }	not over 67
Orissa	3·2	79 }	
Assam	3·2	76	
Madras	4·0	77	
Punjab	4·9	92	50
Central Provinces and Berar	4·9	100	
North-west Frontier Province	4·9	68	
Delhi	4·9	67	
Ajmer-Merwara	6·1	70	
Bombay	7·5	86	83
Sind	8·0	112	

Punjab (for which region the Agrarian Reforms Sub-Committee however got a very different result). Sind is entirely, Punjab almost entirely, dependent upon irrigation water, which is chronically scarce. This situation may have affected Tarlok Singh's method of calculation. Provincial officials in Punjab have stated that where sufficient water is available to grow two crops a year, one man is fully occupied on $2\frac{1}{2}$ ha. (the same has been stated by provincial officials in the North-west Frontier Province of Pakistan). The International Labour Office Advisory Committee for Asia made their estimate higher, but still at only $3\frac{1}{2}$ ha., for the land required to keep a man fully occupied in the double-cropped areas of Pakistan. (In this latter case they specified that two pairs of bullocks would be needed to every three men.)

These Indian figures show how variable is the amount of land required to keep a man occupied. While the rainfall is high (as in Bengal), or on irrigated land where ample supplies of water are available, the figure may be only $2\frac{1}{2}$ ha. On these lands a high proportion of the most labour-demanding crops may be grown. On the lower rainfall lands a higher proportion of the simple cereal crops may be grown, if only for needs of subsistence. Also, as agricultural knowledge advances, labour-saving methods may be introduced, whereby one man can handle a larger area.

The most convenient unit of measurement, where possible, is the number of ha. of cultivated land/adult male engaged in agriculture.[1] Undoubtedly a good deal of agricultural work is done by women, and some by children, particularly in Africa. In some modern countries, including Japan, Germany and France, every farmer's wife is recorded by the Census as a full-time agricultural worker. This appears to be largely for political reasons, to enhance the supposed importance of agriculture in the national economy. As the method of recording female labour varies so greatly between countries, the only statistically safe procedure is to work on male labour only. In Yugoslavia it was estimated (Chapter V) that for each 100 of farm population we should expect 57 man-years of total labour input, if we convert women's and children's labour to adult male equivalents, or 40 units of adult male labour. For most subsistence economies, however, with a higher proportion of children, the number of males engaged in agricultural work may be taken at one-third of total agricultural population. Sometimes we only have figures of total population of a rural area, which include presumably a certain number of village craftsmen and traders. In this case, the number of males engaged in agricultural work may be taken as one-quarter of the whole.

We will also assemble a number of estimates on the extent of underemployment. Relating these to the figures of the amount of land cultivated/man, we can deduce in effect the amount of land required to keep a man fully occupied, in the opinion of the constructors of these estimates.

We need not take into account here regions where the supply of land is clearly abundant. Thus in Mexico[2] agricultural population has been growing at the rate of 25 per cent per decade, but the amount of agricultural land has been expanding at about the same rate, and available land is nearly 10 ha./man.

About the same average prevails for Brazil.[3] The national aver-

---

[1] Cultivated land as defined by FAO, including fallows and orchards. In countries where land is very scarce, it is a reasonable assumption that all land capable of cultivation is being cultivated, and that grazing is confined to mountains, swamps, heathland, etc. But in less crowded countries we must bear in mind that a great deal of land is grazed which would be capable, physically, of arable farming.

[2] *Commercio Exterior*, September 1957.

[3] Lopes, *International Labour Review*, November 1941.

age in 1940 was about 9 ha., falling to $4\frac{1}{2}$ in Sao Paulo, the most developed and the most populated province, and rising to over 30 in Maranhao.

Some of the most intensively cultivated land in the world is in Egypt, where on the average 1·4 crops/year are taken from each unit of land. Even though large quantities of fertilizer are used, it does not appear practicable so far to carry double cropping further than this. Issawi[1] has estimated that the true labour requirements per ha. are 155 man-days (of 10 hours) + 60 women- and child-days. If we take 300 days as the full normal working year, and assume that the ordinary amount of woman and child labour is also available, then land requirements for a man are 1·9 ha. A figure of 2 ha. was also estimated by Bonné.[2]

The present Egyptian figure of only a little over 0·6 ha./man is clearly too low to provide full employment, though not to the extent indicated by the above figures. On a recent official survey of hours worked,[3] if we take a 60-hour week as normal (less public holidays, which had been excluded from the survey), it appears that 42 per cent of the agricultural population were fully occupied at the time of the survey. The average week worked by the whole agricultural population was 79 per cent of the assumed full working week, indicating that, at the present rate of double cropping, 0·8 ha./man would provide full employment. This order of magnitude is indeed confirmed by another statement by Issawi himself. The present state of underemployment, he says, only became apparent during the present century. In the nineteenth century the general complaint in Egypt was of shortage of labour. At that time there was not much double cropping. The figures of ha. of cultivated land/man stood at 1·2 in 1886 and just about 1 at the end of the century. It was only after that date that double cropping became important.

Buck[4] ranged the farms in China by size groups. The smallest had about $\frac{1}{2}$ ha./man, the largest 2. The number of idle months/man-year stood at 1·7 or 1·8 (in mid-winter), almost irrespective of size of farm. It is true, as we have seen in Chapter V, that the occupiers of the smallest farms were driven by poverty to extend their labour to a point where it was bringing in almost zero marginal return; nevertheless these results show that a farm population using

---

[1] C. Issawi, *Egypt at Mid-Century, an Economic Survey*, O.U.P., 1954.
[2] *Economic Development of the Middle East*, 1943.
[3] *International Labour Review*, November 1960.
[4] J. L. Buck, *Land Utilization in China*, 1937.

only hand tools can be fully occupied even on these very small areas.

In Japan also, with an average of only 0·7 ha. cultivated land/man, all the signs indicate very full occupation of men, women, children and old people, although here again labour input has been carried to a point of almost zero marginal return. Much of the 'surplus labour' from small farms finds non-farm employment.[1]

	Japanese Average		Farms below 0·5 Ha. (sample)	
	Male	*Female*	*Male*	*Female*
Number of persons/farm engaged in farm work	1·41	1·45	0·63	0·98
Hours worked/person/year	2306	1770	2810	1377
Of which non-farm work	474	148	1320	238
(average working day about 9 hours)				

A very strong indication that these low land/man ratios are regarded as normal in many parts is shown by the following extraordinary figures from Indonesia.[2]

TABLE XXII. INDONESIA — LAND/MAN RATIOS

HA./MAN ENGAGED IN AGRICULTURE (ASSUMED ¼ OF TOTAL POPULATION)

	Total area	Area of arable land (including estates)	Area harvested (double-crop land counted twice) of food crops plus planted area of commercial crops and estates
West Java	1·07	0·63	0·63
Central Java	0·79	0·59	0·61
East Java	0·97	0·63	0·74
Java and Madura: Total	0·94	0·63	0·65
Outer Islands	18·2	1·3	0·69

In Central Java, where population is very dense, the total land area is only 0·79 ha./man engaged in agriculture, of which 0·59 is cultivated, with a little double cropping. Double cropping appears to be more common in Eastern Java where population density is

[1] Tobata, *Japanese Agriculture*, 1952.
[2] Dr. Hilde Wander, quoting Bino Pusat Statistik, *Penduduk Indonesia*, 1959, and *Statistical Pocketbook of Indonesia*, 1950.

less. But in the Outer Islands of Indonesia, where the amount of land available per person is twenty times what it is in Java, the amount actually harvested per person is hardly any higher. (In the Outer Islands, the figure for arable land is approximately double the figure for harvested land because there is no double cropping, and the cultivators can afford to fallow half their land each year.)

Similar densities are sometimes found in the high rainfall districts in Africa. In Ruanda-Urundi[1] population density rises to 550 persons/sq. km. in some areas. Taking a quarter of the total population as men engaged in agriculture, this gives them approximately $\frac{3}{4}$ ha. each.

Gourou[2] quotes other densely populated areas. The highest densities in Europe are 0·9 ha./man engaged in the Valencia district in Spain, and 0·6 in some parts of southern Italy. The world record appears to be shared by the Adiwerno district in Java, totalling 93 sq. km. in area, engaged in growing sugar cane as well as rice, where the figure falls to 0·24, and by certain areas in Viet Nam.

The highly productive soil area of the delta of the Tonkin in Viet Nam, an area of 15,000 sq. km., is one of the most densely populated agricultural areas in the world. Gourou, who made a study[3] of the human geography of the Delta, recorded an average rural population density (again taking men engaged in agriculture at one-quarter of the whole population) of 0·88 ha./man falling to 0·5 over one-seventh of the area and to 0·24 in a few districts, just matching the figures for the most heavily populated district in Java. The lands of the Tonkinese Delta are exploited with the utmost intensity. Certain techniques practised on these fertile soils consume exceptional quantities of manual labour for the production, wherever possible, of two crops of rice, or one of rice and one of a dry land crop, per year; the help contributed by draught animals is negligible, equipment is neither important nor costly, consisting only of a few tools of wood or bamboo, and land is minutely divided. The poor Tonkinese peasants who inhabit the region work hard for an average of 230 kg. rough rice/person/year supplemented, probably inadequately, by small fish caught in ditches, edible herbs collected off the marshes, fruits, and numerous insects. At this level of food consumption, with a yield of 4

---

[1] P. Gourou, *Memoire de l'Institut Royale Coloniale Belgique*, No. 6, 1953.
[2] P. Gourou, *The Tropical World*, 1961.
[3] P. Gourou, *The Standard of Living in the Delta of the Tonkin*. Institute of Pacific Relations, 9th Conference, French Paper No. 4.

tons rough rice/ha./year, and with 20 per cent of the soil not in rice fields, the land should be capable of feeding a total population of 14 persons/ha. (0·285 ha./man engaged). Where density surpasses this figure, some resources from outside the locality become essential. In these circumstances, income is supplemented by earnings from seasonal migrations to other areas at the time of harvest, or by migrations over a more prolonged period into coal mines on the borders of the Delta, or from peddling.

Other Asian countries with low figures of ha./man engaged in agriculture are Korea and Ceylon with 0·9. Ceylon however still has a large proportion of its total area uninhabited — it is true that this has lower rainfall than the inhabited area, but areas in India and other countries with similar rainfall are capable of supporting large populations. Thailand, Burma, Philippines and Malaya have considerably larger areas of cultivated land for each man in work, and also large areas of potential cultivable land not yet developed at all.

In the Philippines,[1] on a number of sample farms in different provinces, a precise count has been made of the available male labour between the ages of 14 and 65, excluding students and housewives, including the adult male equivalent of other female labour available. Average ha. cultivated land/man equivalent were 1·1. In the low-rainfall area of Cagayan however they were 3·15, and in the little developed province of Mindanao 2·02. This available farm labour was occupied for 20 per cent of its time on non-farm work, and for 47 per cent of its time was unoccupied altogether. In Cagayan and Mindanao, where land was abundant, the proportion of time unoccupied was still 38 and 36 per cent respectively. It seems that we must place this unoccupied time in the category of 'preferred leisure', and conclude that 1 ha./man is regarded as adequate by the Filipinos.

While we are on the question of leisure preference, we may note that the French peasant in the eighteenth century[2] worked less than 200 days a year on his farm. He was also required, on the average, to do about 30 days a year forced labour (Corvee) on roads, etc. Cultivated and pasture land per man engaged in agriculture was about 6 ha.

For India, Qayum[3] estimated that the amount of agricultural

[1] *Farm Management, Land Use and Tenancy in the Philippines*, Central Experiment Station Bulletin No. 1, 1957.
[2] H. de Farcy, *Revue de l'Action Populaire*, April 1962.
[3] Conference on Research in National Income, Delhi, January 1957.

work actually done in 1950–51 was 18·3 billion man-days. He assumed that each man in the rural population could be available for 300 days a year, each women for 120, each adolescent for 150. He then, however, knocked off a round figure of one-third for time required for subsidiary occupations, and concluded that the amount of labour available for agriculture was 26·5 billion man-days. The work actually done was thus almost exactly two-thirds of the available labour. Sen[1] estimated that 'even on the basis of existing antiquated techniques', surplus labour was equivalent to 15 to 20 million workers, or $4\frac{1}{2}$ to 6 billion man-days. If we accept Qayum's figure of the amount of work actually done, Sen's result indicated that this was 78 per cent of the amount of labour available. Underemployment is generally considered to be at its worst in southern India. Srinivasan,[2] surveying seven villages near Coimbatore, assumed 260 days as a normal year. He found that labour utilization as a percentage of actual varied from 53 per cent to 81 per cent, with a median of 65 per cent.

These figures for India however will be considerably modified when we consider below the extreme seasonality of demand of labour in India.

We may now consider land requirements in some of the more densely populated eastern European and Mediterranean climates.

TABLE XXIII. LAND REQUIREMENTS IN SOME OF THE MORE DENSELY POPULATED EASTERN EUROPEAN AND MEDITERRANEAN CLIMATES

| | Ha. agricultural land/male activity engaged in agriculture[a] | |
	1900	1950
Poland	5·9	6·0
Czechoslovakia	4·5	6·9
Hungary	5·4	4·6
Roumania	5·1	3·9
Bulgaria	6·9	3·4
Yugoslavia	5·1	4·5
Italy	3·5	3·6
Spain	7·0	6·2
Portugal	4·2	3·7

[a] These figures include pasture land

[1] World Population Conference, 1954.
[2] *Indian Journal of Agricultural Economics*, April–June 1957.

In these countries, agricultural populations have been declining and the amount of land per head increasing, but there have been exceptions.[1]

In Hungary, for example, cultivated land was only 3·5 ha./male engaged in agriculture in 1938. A variety of estimates have been made of the ratio of actual to potential labour, whose median seems to be about 75 per cent.[2] For Yugoslavia, Krasovic gives the following figures.[3]

TABLE XXIV.   YUGOSLAVIA — LAND/MAN RATIOS

	Ha./man, all agricultural land	Ha./man, cultivated land only
Serbia	3·0	2·2
Voivodina	4·5	3·9
Croatia	3·8	1·9
Slovenia	4·0	1·3
Bosnia-Herzogovina	3·7	1·8
Macedonia	4·1	1·8
Montenegro	5·0	0·6
All Yugoslavia	3·5	2·0

Bicanic[4] estimated for the 1930s labour utilization at 62 per cent of available labour, for the whole country. The same author,[5] in a more detailed study in the 1950s, showed how the smaller holdings sent a larger proportion of their workers to work in the rural industries, which are now becoming distributed around Yugoslavia, as indeed they are also in Japan, and may soon be in India.

Size of holding, ha.	Under 2	2 to 3	3 to 5	5 to 8
Average area, ha.	1·4	2·5	4·0	6·5
Man-year equivalents (women 70% of men) available/ holding	2·68	3·02	3·40	3·53
Do. engaged in non-farm work	0·34	0·28	0·23	0·22

Bicanic estimated the average working year of those engaged in farm work still to be below 2000 hours.

Bulgaria, until recently at any rate, has been a country with comparatively little industrialization and, as population rose, the

[1] F. Dovring, *Land and Labour in Europe, 1900–1950*, The Hague, 1956.
[2] Rudzinski, *Polish Economist*, July–September 1942. Also *The World To-day*, Institute of International Affairs, March 1947.
[3] Krasovic, International Conference of Agricultural Economists, 1955.
[4] Bicanic, *Geographical Review*, January–February 1944.
[5] 1957 Conference of International Association for Research in Income and Wealth; and private communications.

amount of the land per man declined heavily. An estimate for the 1930s[1] showed 355 million man-days of work to be done each year, which, taking 290 days/year as full employment, represented 90 per cent of the available male labour supply, or 63 per cent of male plus female. In the Stara-Zagora district the figure of cultivated land/man fell to 0·8 ha.[2]

Greece,[3] with 3·57 million ha. of farm land (including a limited amount of grassland) in 1960 was estimated to require 86·9 million 'man-productive days' in the busiest three months of the year, with only 84·7 million available, i.e. a deficiency of 2·6 per cent. The authors think that Greece passed from being a country of chronic labour surplus to one of labour deficiency in 1955. However, they define labour availability on the curious assumption, which appears amusing to dwellers in more rainy climates, that 'rainfall of at least 1 millimetre, or rainfall that accumulates less than 1 millimetre and lasts for more than three hours, usually causes the loss of a full day's work'. As we shall see below, there are large seasonal fluctuations in the demand for labour; and also the situation in some of the mountain regions is worse than the national average.

The above figure relates to the supply of man-productive days in the spring quarter of the year. For the whole year 1960 the figure was 357 million. This is calculated on the low basis of 255 days/year, omitting males below 19 and over 65, and with females weighted to convert them into adult male equivalents. The number of male man-years (without weighting ages) was 1·07 million. This implies a ratio of 3½ ha./man (a small amount of pasture is included here). With the number of hours/year devoted to agriculture by the average Greek farmer, this provides something very close to full employment.

For Hungary we have estimates[4] of an average of 200 days actually worked per year on the basis of a 12-hour day. On a 10-hour day we may equate them to 80 per cent and 60 per cent of full employment (300 days). An alternative estimate[5] for 1930, computed on male labour only, indicated actual as 76 per cent of

[1] Egoroff and Mollow, quoted Institut für Konjunkturforschung, Weekly Bulletin, 29 June 1939.
[2] A. Suha, *Economic Problems of Eastern Europe*. This author quotes figures of 1·7 ha./man in the Cracow district of Poland and 1·5 ha./man in a district of Slovakia.
[3] Pepelasis and Yotopoulos, *Surplus Labour in Greek Agriculture, 1953–60*, Centre of Economic Research, Athens, Research Monograph No. 2.
[4] *International Labour Review*, Vol. 25, p. 673 and Vol. 28, p. 525.
[5] Nadujfalvy, *Revue Hongroise de Statistique*, 1947.

potential work. For 1947,[1] on male and female labour taken together, actual employment was estimated at only 53 per cent of potential labour supply. For the Hungarian type of agriculture, which includes a good deal of grazing, it appears that $7\frac{1}{2}$–10 ha./man are necessary in all. Hectares of *cultivated* land/man were 3·3 in 1930 and 2·5 in 1947.

Russia in 1913, with 4 ha. cultivated land/man, was estimated[2] to be 74 per cent occupied: again in 1928,[3] when the area had fallen to 3·6, 78 per cent occupied.

Spain in the 1930s was estimated[4] to have $7\frac{1}{2}$ per cent complete unemployment and 5 per cent partial among rural workers. At this time cultivated land/man was 5 ha. For 1903–12 an estimate[5] of actual at 83 per cent of potential employment was made.

In Italy in 1951–2[6] rural working population (of whom a few are female) included 4·93 million occupiers of land, who lost on an average 88 days/year, and 1·88 million wage workers who lost on an average 150 days/year, out of an assumed total of 275 potential working days. The weighted mean of days lost was therefore 94 (63 in the north, 112 in central Italy, 117 in the south and islands). A higher pre-war degree of utilization is shown[7] by Vitali and Angelini, with the average rural worker and farmer estimated to be working 2250 and 2500 hours/year respectively, as against a supposed norm of 3000.

Italy in 1950 had 3·6 ha. agricultural land/man engaged, as shown in Dovring's table, and only 2·3 ha. cultivated land. From the above estimates of underemployment we may conclude that 3·5 ha. cultivated land/man engaged and 5·5 ha. total land are necessary for full employment, with Italian-style agriculture — not quite as intensive as Greek. (It is worth recollecting that Cato in *De Re Rustica* stated that one full-time man was necessary for every 4·8 ha. of olive or 1·6 ha. of vineyard.)

There appears, however, to be some uniformity between the figures for Mediterranean countries. In the Mediterranean, cereal harvesting is generally completed by June, and is followed by a hot dry spell, in which some underoccupation is likely, though less so

[1] Meszaroa, *Statisztika Szemle*, 1952.
[2] Marcus, *International Labour Review*, Vol. 53, p. 356.
[3] *International Labour Review*, Vol. 27, p. 349.
[4] De Arlandis, *Weltwirtschaftliches Archiv*, September 1936.
[5] Vandellos, *Metron*, 1925.
[6] *Banca Nazionale del Lavoro*, June 1955.
[7] Quoted in *Foreign Agriculture*, United States Department of Agriculture, May 1945.

if there is a grape harvest to be gathered. The League of Nations Conference on European Rural Life in 1939 concluded that $5\frac{1}{2}$ ha./man engaged was inadequate in Lithuania, but that 2 ha. was not seriously inadequate in east Flanders. An adequate system of transport and communication (they might also have added an abundant supply of fertilizers) makes all the difference, in making possible more labour-intensive crops and livestock than those of less developed peasant populations.

Any plans for the permanent diversion of this rural labour surplus into other employments come up against the fact that it is not available throughout the year. It is true that the better distributed the rainfall, the better distributed also the demand for labour; but even where rainfall is uniform, there are still peak demands. Issawi suggested that his estimate of the proportion of available Egyptian agricultural labour occupied might be raised in the ratio of 3:2 if availability in peak periods only were considered.

TABLE XXV.   UTILIZATION OF LABOUR IN AGRICULTURE
AS PERCENTAGE OF AVAILABLE LABOUR SUPPLY

| | | India | | Ghana[e] | Iraq[c] | |
| | | Madhya[a] | Maha- | Cocoa | Middle | Best area |
Month	China[d]	Pradesh	rashtra[b]	farming	Tigris	(Diyala)
January	47	29	65	57	22	24
February	78	29	62	18	23	27
March	94	41	66	30	23	26
April	97	41	32	28	35	39
May	98	52	34	30	70	92
June	96	33	42	30	72	94
July	94	127	55	47	56	76
August	96	127	60	57	60	76
September	97	93	47	75	52	43
October	92	96	52	100	53	45
November	82	82	100	90	54	52
December	57	82	94	65	25	35

Note: Figures in excess of 100 indicate temporary agricultural work done by non-agricultural workers of the village.

[a] Shiwalkar, *Indian Journal of Agricultural Economics*, March 1954 (refers to periods beginning about the middle of the months specified).

[b] Institute of Agriculture, Anand. Bulletin No. 4, March 1958.

[c] Hunting Technical Services. Final Report to the Government of Iraq, Diyala and Middle Tigris Project.

[d] Calculated from Buck, *Land Utilization in China*, Statistical Appendix.

[e] Beckett, London School of Economics Monograph on Social Anthropology, No. 10.

In some parts of India, where the rainy season is very short, this peaks the demand for labour in a most alarming manner. Instead of being in embarrassing surplus, labour suddenly becomes the critically scarce factor of production. If any able-bodied man or woman is incapacitated by illness (e.g. the malaria which is prevalent in many of these countries) during this period, the loss of production may be very serious. Experience in some European countries such as Italy and Greece shows that the cultivation of fruit and the keeping of livestock spread the demand for labour better over the year. These countries too, however, have a problem of labour shortage at the peak period.

The Chinese government have recently discovered these facts, to their cost. Paradoxical though it may seem, they have created a labour shortage in China. Even at the time of Buck's enquiry, 65 per cent of the villages reported some labour shortage at harvest time. Only 19 per cent of the villages reported that they never experienced labour shortage.

The distribution of work throughout the year of Chinese farms was carefully investigated by Buck who showed that the average amount of time lost was only 15 per cent (1·8 months); and that this was practically confined to the winter months.

But Mao had other sources of information. 'Under present conditions of production', he wrote in his book, *Socialist Upsurge*, 'there would be a one-third manpower surplus in rural areas.' And, having written it, he probably believed it. Possibly he was basing his judgement on India, where only two-thirds of the available labour is occupied. But in comparison with China, this might be called 'technical unemployment'; India is more 'technically advanced' then China, using ox ploughs which require less labour.

Never has a mistake in information on agricultural economics had more serious consequences. It was the belief in the existence of this 'one-third surplus' of labour among the rural population which led to the massive diversion of rural labour to all sorts of other projects during the 'Great Leap Forward' which began in 1958, many of them quite futile, such as the rural blast furnaces which had to have most of their materials carried by hand, and ended up by yielding an unusable product. It was this artificially created labour shortage which has been primarily responsible for the food shortages of subsequent years, not floods and droughts.

It is not that Mao did not have warning. Ma Yin-Chu, President of the University of Peking, one of the few independent thinkers in

China (he believes that population growth should be restricted) pointed out[1] that there were critical labour shortages at a vital period of the year described by the Chinese proverb 'in the morning yellow, in the evening green' (when peasants are harvesting the first rice crop, but having to transplant the seedlings for the second rice crop in the cool of the evening of the same day). Even in 1956, the government had ordered excessive planting in Chekiang Province beyond the capacity of the labour available, with the result that transplantation of the second crop was not performed over a wide area, and over a larger area was left very late, with consequent very low crop yields.

For China, Ma Yin-Chu advocated the use of machinery — 'The future key to rich increases to rural production', he wrote, 'is in mechanical assistance during the excessively busy period.' He may have been right, if the demand for labour in China is really very sharply peaked: though the matter requires very careful examination, in view of the capital cost involved.

It has been proposed elsewhere that cultivators of small areas in Asia should proceed, not directly to large tractors, but to small power cultivators of five horse-power or so. Some such are beginning to make their appearance in Japan, where we may see a direct transition from hand to mechanical cultivation, without an intervening period of cultivation with animal power. Wijewardene[2] contends that the operations of the farmer may be 'limited by the tractive power of his bullocks' even on farms as small as 2 ha. For farms between this size and some 15 ha. he recommends small power cultivators; for larger farms full-size tractors can presumably be used. The capital cost would be somewhere between that of one and two pairs of bullocks.

It is doubtful however whether Wijewardene has made his case for farms as small as 2 ha. Even if the whole area were cultivated for rice or sugar cane, the most demanding crops, needing six or eight cultivations, such a farm would require only 400–500 hours of work yearly by a pair of bullocks. In addition, he forgets that bullocks are very necessary for transport in many parts of Asia.

The above estimate was based on information received in India about the rate at which oxen can work in rice cultivation on muddy land. On dry land (if not breaking it for the first time) a pair of

---

[1] *New Construction*, Peking, November 1959 (Chinese text). We are indebted to Dr. K. R. Walker, School of Oriental Studies, University of London, for these quotations.

[2] R. Wijewardene, *World Crops*, Vol. 13, No. 11, November 1961.

oxen should be able to plough a hectare in 20 hours. Even in countries with a short monsoon season therefore it is only on the largest farms that the farmer is likely to find himself seriously 'limited by the tractive power of his bullocks'.

In Uganda,[1] including all operations, hand cultivation is esti-mated to require 25 man days/ha. of able-bodied labour; with the ploughing and harrowing done by oxen, 16 man-days (including some boy labour). Ploughing has not given the results hoped for in increasing acreage cultivated, or yields per acre.

The unevenness of labour demand throughout the year was one of the subjects of Fuggles Couchman's pioneer study.[2] On his recommended holding of $3\frac{1}{4}$ ha. (8 acres) the number of man-days/month required was as follows: November, 24; December, 15; January, $30\frac{1}{2}$; February, $39\frac{1}{2}$; March, $33\frac{1}{2}$; April, $18\frac{1}{2}$; May, $14\frac{1}{2}$; June, $15\frac{1}{4}$. It appears that the harvest was gathered from July onwards, but that this work could be spread. The February peak should be within the capacity of a man and wife both working on the holding; but, the author added (using the sort of language which would not now be regarded as permissible), 'natives do not usually work a full eight-hour day . . . a second wife and children would enable the work to be kept well in hand.'

Clayton[3] made most interesting proposals for planning an East African (Kenya) farm of 4·3 ha. The farm family contained three adults deemed all to be capable of working an eight-hour day for 300 days a year, or a potential labour input of 7200 man-hours/year in all. A programme designed by the government for such a farm yielded an annual income of £301, equivalent to only 3 kg. maize/man hour *available* (appreciably more per man-hour actually worked but still a low real income). Clayton prepared a linear pro-gramme which raised the net revenue to £334, leaving (after pro-viding 500 hours for necessary maintenance) 1388 hours still unused, mostly in the May–September period. This now repre-sents a return of 4·1 kg. of maize equivalent/hour actually worked (compare returns of 2·0 to 2·6 kg. maize equivalent/man-hour found by Couchman in the 1930s). An improved linear programme raises the net income to £388. These programmes are based on the hiring of draught oxen; a proposal to use a hired tractor in prepar-ing the seed bed ended up with a slight debit balance. A final pro-

---

[1] Tothill, *Agriculture in Uganda*, O.U.P., 1940.
[2] F. Couchman, *East African Journal of Agriculture*, March 1939.
[3] E. S. Clayton, 'Economic and Technical Optima in Peasant Agriculture', *Journal of Agricultural Economics*, May 1961.

gramme employed all the labour available, except for the 500 hours maintenance, to be done in the off season. However, the average return per man-hour of labour actually worked was reduced to 3·85 kg. of maize. The marginal return for the 1388 man-hours saved by more refined programming thus works out at only 2·75 kg. maize/hour. The African may prefer to work these additional hours for a marginal return lower than his average; or he may prefer more leisure. But at any rate he should be grateful for the information in helping him to decide.

Fully mechanized cereal farming[1] has begun in East Africa. It is recommended that such farms should be of 200 ha., with £1200 capital in buildings and £6070 in equipment, similar to large farms in England. Labour input is only 40 man-hours/ha. (half of which is in harvesting) and gross product 28 kg. wheat/man-hour. Labourers are paid 1 kg. maize equivalent/man-hour and tractor drivers 1·35; costs, excluding rent and interest (mainly fertilizers and depreciation), amount to £20/ha., of which labour constitutes only 6½ per cent. Even on these low wages, at a yield of 1·12 tons/ha., such wheat growing would be barely remunerative, if the wheat were sold at world price (£25 approximately delivered Europe, with large land and sea transport costs to be met).

An interesting and simple example quoted by Isobe[2] compares a farm of 1·9 ha., with 2·8 man equivalent labour units, growing single-cropped rice, vetch and mulberry, with a slightly smaller farm of 1·5 ha., and 2·4 labour units, growing double-cropped rice, wheat, barley, vetch, fruit and vegetables, and keeping poultry. Both require a certain amount of animal draught power, between April and June, though the second is better spread, not exceeding 20 hours per week, while the former may require nearly 40. The second farm is able to spread its labour requirements far better; they fall below 100 man-hours/week only for 5 weeks a year, and have temporary maxima just under 150 in June and September. The former farm on the other hand has a violent labour peak of over 300 hours required in the first week in June, and another peak in October, while for much of the winter less than ten hours a week are required.

A particularly thorough study was made by Kitsopanides[3] in the

---

[1] *Wheat Production in Kenya, 1955–56, an Economic Study*, Government Printer, Nairobi, 1957.
[2] *Farm Planning with special reference to the management and improving of small-scale family farming*, Japanese Ministry of Agriculture, October 1956.
[3] G. Kitsopanides, privately communicated.

CHART XI.

LABOUR DISTRIBUTION OF TWO FARMS
IN TOYAMA PREFECTURE, JAPAN

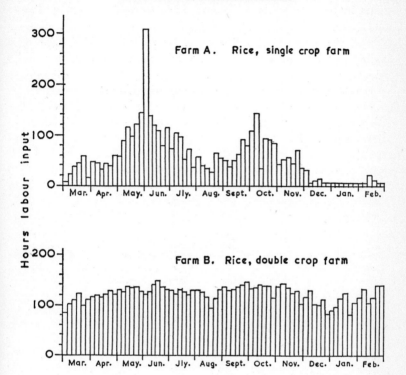

	Farm A	Farm B
Available labour on farm (man equivalents)	2.8	2.4
Size of farm (hectares)	1.9	1.5

Florina district of Greek Macedonia, a mountainous district right on the Albanian border, where we would expect the problems of underemployment to be worse than for Greece as a whole. For the first time, it appears, he has measured the amount of time devoted by the women to domestic labour, indicating the amount of time left available for farm work. Of the available time of the able-bodied women, 38 per cent is occupied in domestic work, and the remainder is available for farm work. In the busy summer months

K

the women are able to defer a certain amount of the domestic work until the winter. Greek law requires children to be educated, but law and custom permit a certain amount of farm work to be done by the children (estimated at 16 hours in May, 18 hours in June, 36 hours in July, 50 hours in August, 22 hours in September). The average farm is 5 ha., and has 1·84 able-bodied men and 2·05 able-bodied women (the latter treated as the equivalent of 1·54 able-bodied men). Sundays and public holidays are excluded from the calculations of available labour supply. In a mountainous region, with considerable snowfall, only 5 hours/day of work is considered possible in the winter months; but this is offset by expecting 12 hours/day in the summer. Even so, underemployment in the winter is marked.

TABLE XXVI. LABOUR REQUIREMENTS IN A
MOUNTAINOUS DISTRICT OF NORTHERN GREECE

Month	Available labour[b]	Domestic labour	Family labour on farm[c]	Family labour not required on farm or in home	of which employed elsewhere	Unoccupied family labour as % of available	Non-family labour hired on farms
			Hours/man equivalent[a]/month				
January	216	70	35	111	21	42	—
February	221	64	54	103	26	35	—
March	250	67	78	105	27	31	5
April	275	73	90	112	25	32	6
May	320	63	132	125	21	33	18
June	341	56	193	92	19	21	26
July	347	51	246	50	15	10	25
August	382	55	240	57	15	12	20
September	319	59	168	92	18	23	11
October	275	66	113	96	30	24	10
November	250	68	49	113	39	37	1
December	216	73	38	105	29	35	—
	3380	716	1438	1226	295	28	124

[a] Women treated as 0·75 man-units.
[b] Sundays and public holidays are excluded from the calculations of available labour supply.
[c] Child labour included in the high figures for the summer months: maximum assumed for the man himself, 300 hours/month.

Farm family members, it will be seen, do a certain amount of work away from their own farms; while at the same time a certain amount of hired labour is engaged in the busy season, much of it coming across the mountains from Yugoslavia.

These cases of extreme congestion or 'rural overpopulation'

represent an unhappy by-road from the normal course of economic development. But the country travelling down this road may reach a point of no return. The normal and fortunate course of economic development is that, when the productivity of a country's agriculture can considerably exceed the required standards of consumption of the rural population, and when other circumstances are favourable too, urban and industrial population begins to grow. Some of the goods and services which the urban population can supply may in their turn contribute a good deal, as we shall see shortly, to the further productivity of agriculture. But if this normal urban growth is in some way checked, and rural population continues to grow so that the amount of cultivable land per man falls, marginal productivity may also fall, and then, even though standards of consumption per head may fall, the difference between production and consumption, and in consequence the ability to feed an urban population, also diminishes. Such a country may therefore become relatively more dependent upon agriculture than ever. We then see a substantial proportion of the rural population having just about enough to eat but not much of anything else, unoccupied or unemployed for many months of the year. Such a situation is of course accentuated if the climate is difficult, as in India.

This state of affairs, so regrettably common in the present-day world, was also — this is not generally recognized — the lot of rural England for a long period, probably for several centuries, in the past. In 1688 Gregory King estimated that, out of a total population of 5·5 million, 1·3 million represented 'cottagers and paupers' and their families, a seriously underoccupied rural population, receiving an average family income less than half that of a regularly employed labourer. This persistent rural unemployment in England did not disappear until the middle of the nineteenth century, and in Ireland is present to this day. It required a rapid growth of urban employment relative to population — more rapid than that of which the seventeenth and eighteenth centuries were capable — to solve this problem, even in a country so favourably situated as England.

But urbanization, or to use a more precise phrase, the development of non-agricultural employment generally, is not to be had just for the asking. We know that it requires a combination of factors, not always easily brought about, to make such development possible. We have clear evidence that England in 1688 or

Germany in 1800 had an agriculture which, though very unproductive by present-day standards, nevertheless could produce a good deal more than was required for the food consumption of the rural population.

Even in the ancient world similar relationships prevailed. When population had passed a certain density, an urban civilization generally developed, producing manufactured goods which it traded in order to obtain primary products from more distant areas. A state of rural overpopulation can best be defined and considered in the light of the converse phenomenon, failure of an adequate urban population to develop. The most striking examples of this, indeed, are in countries which we know to have had a great urban development in ancient times, but which have failed in the modern world to establish even that degree of urbanization which they possessed in the remote past, e.g. Egypt, Greece, the Indus valley, the centres of the Maya, Aztec and Inca civilizations in America.

This phenomenon of rural overpopulation is in some ways analogous to the phenomenon of super-cooling or of metastable equilibrium in physics or chemistry. We seem to settle down for a considerable period in a situation considerably removed from that demanded by true economic equilibrium. We may perhaps press the analogy further to predict that, once the metastable equilibrium is disturbed, the progress towards true equilibrium will then be rapid.

It is hard to give any generalized reason as to why this state of affairs should come about. On the whole we must seek for political and historical rather than for narrowly economic reasons. Historically, some deficiency in the political order often prevented or impeded the development of towns and of commercial activities. In many cases this can be attributed to the despotic rule of absolute monarchies, particularly where arbitrary and oppressive taxation is imposed, as was particularly the case in all territories formerly part of the Turkish Empire. To take another example, in the eleventh century south Italy and Sicily supported a great many more people per unit area than Belgium, and apparently at a considerably higher standard of living. Their subsequent lapse into a state of underemployment, from which they have not recovered to this day, must probably be blamed upon political factors.

CHAPTER VIII

Consistency

Re-expressing all incomes, and all kinds of consumption, of food and of other products, in grain equivalents, using direct data of supplies of agricultural products in some cases, converting into grain on a world standard scale of relative prices, revaluing money data for incomes and consumption, in effect in terms of the relative prices prevailing on the local markets, is a procedure which would not be a permissible form of economic analysis in high-income countries. The distortions which might be introduced by changes in the price of grain, not accompanied by changes in the prices of other products, would be very serious. This procedure can be tolerated, however, in countries where real incomes are low enough for the supply and consumption of grain to represent a large proportion of all income and expenditure.

We have some idea of minimum requirements for physiological well-being, and we must also bear in mind that in many parts of the world there will be a large number of people who, at any given time, are consuming less than this. As the incomes of people at or near subsistence level rise, we naturally expect them to consume more food. But even in their case we should not expect, nor do we in fact find, that the whole of such an increase in income will be used for food consumption. The non-food purchases which such families have to make are also of considerable urgency, and these expenditures also may be expected to rise quite markedly as soon as a rise in income allows it (apart from the occasional case of a very poor family which has a high fixed commitment for house rent or some such expenditure). If, as may be the case with the most needy family, both food and non-food expenditure tend to rise in the same proportion as income rises, this implies an income elasticity of demand for food equal to one. We are not likely in fact to find quite such a high figure for income elasticity, though we find a few figures approaching it for the very poorest families.

Studying the relationship between real income and food consumption in a large number of economically advanced, and also middle- and low-income countries, Jones and Basu,[1] after testing hyperbolae and a number of other possible mathematical relationships, concluded that the best fit to the data was obtained by a function which made food consumption vary with the logarithm of real income. (Consumption of cereal was best expressed by an equation containing a negative exponential, i.e. rising to a maxi-

CHART XII.

INCOME ELASTICITY OF DEMAND FOR FOOD

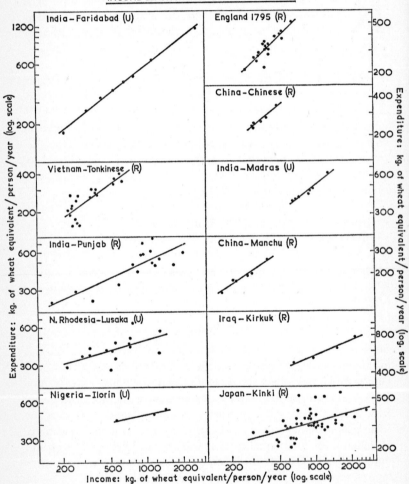

[1] 'International Pattern of Demand for Foodstuffs in 1954', *Farm Economist*, Oxford, 1957.

mum at a certain specified income level, and falling beyond that
point.) This relationship necessarily implies that income elasticity
must fall steadily, in inverse proportion to the quantity of food
consumption, as real incomes increase.

At the lowest levels of income, however, which concern us at
present, this relationship does not appear to hold. Income elasticities
of demand for food, though varying in a surprising way between
communities in various countries and times which, on the face of it,

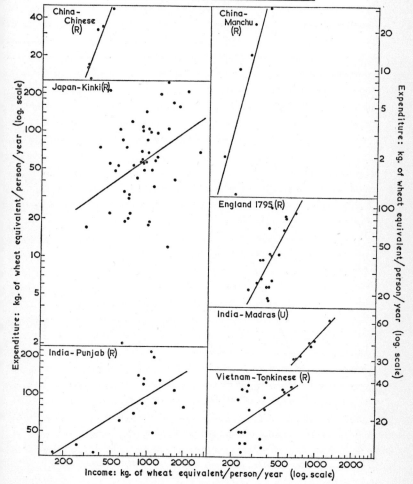

CHART XIII.

INCOME ELASTICITY OF DEMAND FOR CLOTHING

have been suffering a similar degree of poverty, nevertheless in the study of different families within a single community appear to be fairly constant over the range of real income observed. Instead of looking for a semi-logarithmic relationship such as Jones and Basu found, therefore, it appeared best to express both income (largely income in kind, though there may be a cash-income component) and consumption of food as a whole, expressed in kg. grain equivalent/person/year, by their logarithms. If the relationship

CHART XIV.

INCOME ELASTICITIES OF DEMAND I

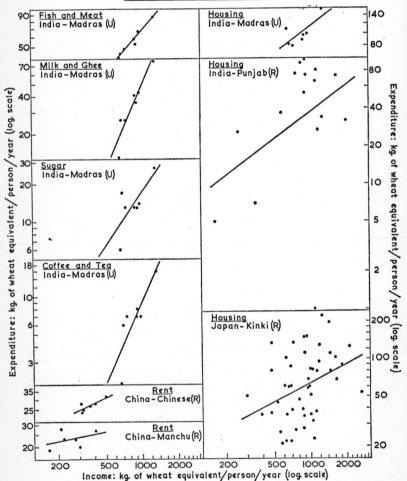

between the two appears to be approximately linear, as it is in nearly all cases, then the slope of the line, on such a logarithmic diagram, gives a direct measurement of the income elasticity of demand for food.

Budget data obtained by Gourou on the income and expenditure of a number of poor Tonkinese peasants and small peasant prorprietors, have been converted into economic wheat equivalents.[1]

CHART XV.

INCOME ELASTICITIES OF DEMAND II

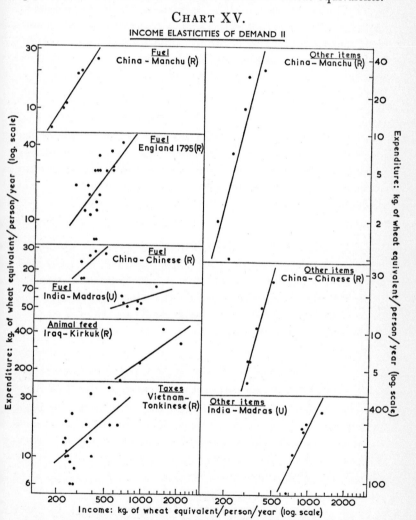

[1] P. Gourou, *The Standard of Living in the Delta of the Tonkin*, Institute of Pacific Relations, 9th Conference, French Paper No. 4.

The high-income elasticity of demand for food is clearly seen in the diagram. Gourou emphasizes that the land here is supporting so dense a population at subsistence level only that no significant surplus is being produced for clothing, housing or other objects. He does, however, make the interesting comment that the mountains framing this plain are very lightly populated — three to four persons per sq. km. — and that apparently there is no lack of room for Tonkinese colonization; but fertile soils are rare, and malaria — non-existent in the Tonkinese Delta — is rampant in the mountains, causing widespread ill-health. Although in a normal year 60 per cent of the population are barely sustained, and require only slightly unfavourable conditions to suffer actual shortage of food, Gourou states that processions of starving people are not seen in Tonkin; this he attributes to the security they have in their family and village environment.

It is an interesting sidelight on the difficulties encountered in persuading peasants from overcrowded Java to migrate to the less populated outer islands, that those who have a minimum of 218 kg. of economic wheat equivalent per head per year available for food consumption are not likely to migrate,[1] which suggests that at this low level of living causal inter-relationships include non-economic factors.

Japan, where densities of population are also high, has a surprisingly low income elasticity of demand for food. Data recorded for 49 family farms in Kinki district in 1956[2] imply a customary level of food consumption which is little affected by increases in income. In Japan non-food consumer goods are readily available, at low prices; this factor probably affects the willingness of peasant families to spend money on food.

Dittmer attempted to give a picture of real economic pressure in a budget study of 100 Chinese families and 95 Manchu families located some five miles outside Peking. Of these, only one-third were cultivators; a further third had trades, one-sixth were small dealers, and one-sixth were labourers. The material was collected between 1914 and 1918 and included destitute Manchu families who had formerly lived in the area in opulence on tribute money exacted from the conquered Chinese.[3]

[1] Pelzer, *Pioneer Settlement in the Asiatic Tropics*, New York, 1954.
[2] Kyoto University, Research Institute of Farm Accounting, No. 1. *The Report of Investigation of Family Farm Economy in 1956, Kinki District*, Japan, 1959.
[3] C. G. Dittmer, 'An Estimate of the Standard of Living in China', *Quarterly Journal of Economics*, Vol. XXXIII, November 1918, No. 1.

Income elasticity of demand for clothing and fuel is seen to be high in this cold north China climate. Women and children infested fields and highways picking up sticks, and collecting dry grass and leaves, in an endeavour to prevent families from freezing to death; there was a marked tendency among the Manchus to increase expenditure on fuel with increases in income. The graph clearly illustrates Dittmer's findings that many families maintained a 'starvation standard', and were thrust into debt simply through buying the most pressing necessities of life. It should be borne in mind, however, that this is an estimate of the standard of living in the less productive, colder, corn-growing north. Conditions among rural communities in the rich rice soil areas of central and south China are unlikely to have been so severe.

For purposes of comparison, the income elasticity of demand for food and drink of agricultural wage labourers in England has been calculated from budget data contained in Eden's *The State of the Poor* published in 1797.[1] Enclosure had deprived the agricultural labourer of various sources by which he could supplement his wages — his fuel from waste land, his cow and pig on the common pasture, a strip under a crop in the common fields; and an industrial revolution had swept away the earnings of his family from village crafts. He had become merely a wage-earner. Many families were frequently in great distress, often in debt, and sometimes without bread, living almost entirely upon barley and water, and a few potatoes. The high-income elasticity of demand for food and drink includes, however, a relatively high expenditure on beer and meat on the part of families who could afford them. We may see here some 'demonstration effect' from the example of wealthier families; and also perhaps, in contrast to modern Japan, the effect of the scarcity and high prices of industrially produced consumption goods.

Similar farming systems prevail in the Punjab and in central Iraq, in which draught animals are used for cultivation, and wheat is the predominant grain; animals are also kept for the supply of milk and milk products. Figures of net income and expenditure were extracted from family budget studies of peasant proprietors, who represent the typical peasant of the Punjab (India) working in the hill and sub-montane regions and in the plains, where all the chief means of irrigation, i.e. well, canal, as well as rainfed farming

[1] F. Morton Eden, *The State of the Poor*, 1797.

are found.[1] In this sample, an average of 41 per cent of total expenditure was for purchased goods and services, including education in the higher income groups; the relatively wide range of consumer goods and services available to these people is reflected in the low-income elasticity of demand for food. Nevertheless, in an economy based on peasant proprietorship of settled holdings in which ploughs and work animals are employed and financial resources are required, productivity may remain low, and the moneylender fulfil a major role.

TABLE XXVII. INCOME ELASTICITY OF DEMAND FOR FOOD

Rural communities	Year of survey		
England[a]	1795	Agricultural wage labour	0·92
Vietnam[a]	1938	Poor Tonkinese peasants	0·69
China (north)[b]	1914–18	Chinese peasants	0·77
China (north)[b]	1914–18	Manchu peasants	0·63
Iraq[b]	1958	Settlers: Kirkuk irrigation project	0·40
India — Punjab[a]	1953–54	Peasant proprietors	0·44
Japan — Kinki[a]	1956	Family farms	0·25
Urban communities			
India — Faridabad[b]	1954	Indian National Sample Survey	0·74
India — Madras[b]	1935–36	Working-class (cotton mill) families	0·73
Africa — N. Rhodesia[a]	1947	Lusaka: urban African wage-earners	0·27

[a] Based on individual family budget data   [b] Based on income groups

The urban surveys in Madras and Faridabad gave a much higher income elasticity of demand for food than for the Punjab cultivators, which suggests that the latter are a relatively rich community in an absolutely poor country.

It is interesting to compare the Punjab results with those of the closely settled peasant cultivators of the Kirkuk Irrigation Project in central Iraq, where external grazing is scarce and some grain must be fed to livestock even at low levels of production.[2] In a

[1] Punjab Board of Economic Enquiry, Publication No. 39, *Family Budgets of Nineteen Cultivators in the Punjab, 1953–54.*
[2] P. E. Naylor, 'A Farm Survey of the New Hawija Settlement Project in Central Iraq', *Journal of Agricultural Economics*, Vol. XIV, No. 1, June 1960; and privately communicated.

study of the economic conditions of the settlers, Naylor found that the farming system is determined by the prevailing climatic conditions and the seasonality of irrigation water supplies. The climate is semi-arid with a long dry season. It is a low rainfall and total precipitation varies widely between one year and another; and irrigation water supplies are dependent upon highly seasonal natural river flows. The land is farmed under a simple fallow rotation mainly for the production of wheat and barley — crops which the settlers were accustomed to growing under rainfed conditions before joining the Project, so that the only additional skills which they required were for irrigation.

Many of the farmers were nomadic tribesmen before they settled on the Project, and have a considerable head of stock; even so livestock management tends to remain an entirely separate entity, and no attempt is made to integrate it into the farming system. Animals are used for ploughing and transport and to some extent for meat, milk, ghee and wool. The proportion of gross output which is consumed on the holding as food, feed and seed is a factor which strongly influences the volume of sales. Human consumption of staple cereals does not rise with a rise in output, but remains fairly constant; but the income elasticity of demand for grain for live-stock feed is as high as 0·70 in a situation in which grazing is a scarce resource. Fruit, vegetables, and oilseeds consumed rise approximately as output rises. The consumption of livestock products in the household not only rises more or less in proportion to output, but much more than proportionately to livestock output alone. Taking all products together, Naylor found that home consumption rises as output rises, but less than proportionately, the increased income being spent on the higher valued products, including tea and sugar. He forecasts that the quantity and value of home-consumed produce will decrease absolutely as production becomes further oriented towards the market and farm income increases — the settler purchasing his food requirements instead in the market. He observes, however, that this step does not appear to have been taken yet even among the richer settlers, partly because of the comparative inaccessibility of markets, and partly because the absolute level of income is still too low.

Using data from 171 families interviewed in an urban consumer survey at Ilorin,[1] Heads set out to demonstrate how the interaction

[1] J. Heads, 'Urbanization and Economic Progress in Nigeria', *South African Journal of Economics*, Vol. 27, No. 3, September 1959.

between a rise in agricultural productivity, and the low income elasticity of demand for food, has allowed the growth of secondary and tertiary industry and increased urbanization in Nigeria. He found also that, at high-income levels, imported foods tended to become relatively more important in food budgets, and the income elasticity of demand for home-produced foodstuffs is even less than the total income elasticity of demand for food.

Thomson's study of an urban community in Northern Rhodesia[1] also indicates the low income elasticity of demand for food; she found that the money spent on food tends to be a residual after meeting other requirements such as clothes, furniture or household utensils, indicating a decided preference for non-food items. She also noted a tendency for increased consumption of 'luxury' foods such as tea, sugar, cooking oil and tinned milk, in the higher-income households.

Among unskilled labourers in Mbale, Uganda, the lowest-income families, living at a level of about 350–400 kg. wheat equivalent/person/year, and spending 55 per cent of their incomes on food, had an income elasticity of demand for food of one.[2] At higher-income levels it had fallen to 0·6, and over the whole range was 0·8.

Mandal found in a West Bengal village[3] that easy access to market opportunities brought within reach of the community a variety of consumption goods, and induced a larger sale of paddy, even among the poorer farmers, who badly wanted money for purchasing these goods.

Income elasticity studies for a range of consumption goods among Madras working-class families demonstrate the desire for washing soap, newspapers and amusements. The relatively high income elasticity of demand for food can be further broken down for specific items as follows:

Fish and meat	1·11
Milk and ghee	2·24
Sugar	1·40
Coffee and tea	2·19

An income elasticity of demand for food as high as 0·64 is quoted

[1] B. P. Thomson, *Two Studies in African Nutrition: an urban and a rural community in Northern Rhodesia*, Rhodes Livingstone Paper No. 24, 1954.
[2] *Patterns of Income Expenditure and Consumption of African Unskilled Workers in Mbale*, East African Statistical Department, Uganda Unit, 1958.
[3] G. C. Mandal, 'The Marketable Surplus of Aman Paddy in East Indian Villages', *Indian Journal of Agricultural Economics*, Vol. XVI, January–March 1961.

by the Ivory Coast Government dealing with high-paid men in Abijan,[1] with income levels ranging from 600 kg. wheat equivalent/person/year and upwards; more significant, however, are the even higher income elasticities of demand for drink and non-food items, i.e. drink 1·14, tobacco 0·72, services and travel 1·11, urban transport 1·13, dress 2·13, durables 2·70, and rent 0·52.

Generally high figures for income elasticity of demand for food by urban communities in Africa are shown by Kaneda and Johnston.[2] For both Abidjan and Mbale a figure of 0·69 is estimated (similar to those obtained here), 0·69 also for Nairobi, and 0·58 for Salisbury. Figures of 0·74–0·86 for three cities in Ghana, however, appear rather hard to accept. Information appears to have been collected to a large extent from petty traders, by inadequately qualified interviewers, and in some cases without enquiry into incomes.

It is worth noting variations in income elasticities between commodities, in urban and rural communities in the Philippines.[3] Income elasticities for subsistence requirements of rice and corn are inelastic since their consumption is well satisfied even at low-income levels. Income elasticities are generally higher for specific items such as canned whole milk, as will be seen from the following figures.

TABLE XXVIII. PHILIPPINES: INCOME ELASTICITIES BETWEEN COMMODITIES

Products	Urban-Rural Sector	Income Elasticity
Rice	Manila	·001
	Urban	·120
	Rural	− ·149
Maize	Manila	− ·051
	Urban	·103
	Rural	·013
Bakery products	Manila	·367
	Urban	·396
	Rural	·605

[1] *Les Budgets Familiaux des Salaries Africains en Abidjan*, Cote d'Ivoire, August–September 1956, p. 83.

[2] Hiromitsu Kaneda and Bruce F. Johnston, 'Urban Food Expenditure Patterns in Tropical Africa', *Food Research Institute Studies*, Vol. II, No. 3, November 1961.

[3] 'The Philippines: Long-term Projection of Supply and of Demand for Selected Agricultural Products', ERS-Foreign-34, United States Department of Agriculture.

Products	Urban-Rural Sector	Income Elasticity
Fresh milk and milk products	Manila	·649
	Urban	·899
	Rural	− ·022
Canned whole milk	Manila	1·588
	Urban	1·277
	Rural	·406
Pork	Manila	·380
	Urban	·413
	Rural	·212
Fresh beef	Manila	·555
	Urban	·388
	Rural	·124
Poultry	Manila	·176
	Urban	·393
	Rural	·258
Fish and fish products	Manila	·153
	Urban	·272
	Rural	·329
Cotton yarn	Manila	·011
	Urban	·283
	Rural	·181
Other fibres	Manila	·624
	Urban	·206
	Rural	·319

It will be seen from the diagram that there are considerable differences in the income elasticities of demand for food among peasant producers. The highest slope, other than for England in 1795, is about 0·77. The line for Japan is striking; it follows a very low slope throughout its length, indicating an income elasticity of 0·25 — the wealthier Japanese peasants are content with the same food that they used to eat when they were poorer. Though at a higher level, the same considerations seem also to apply to urban Japanese. Noda[1] deduced from time series an income elasticity of demand for food in Japan of 0·6 between 1878 and 1921, falling to 0·2 between 1922 and 1937.

It may be perhaps that in the Indian towns, and in eighteenth-century England, there is a so-called 'demonstration effect', of abundant spending on food by the wealthier families, which leads the poorer families to spend a substantial proportion of any income increase, if they obtain it, also on food.

[1] Quoted by Johnston and Mellor, Food Research Institute Studies, November 1960; in Japanese, 1959.

A number of figures which have been published for India, based on family budget data, imply even higher income elasticities, of 0·9 or more. Most of these results are vitiated by a rather subtle fallacy. Most of these budget studies state income and expenditure per family. But an Indian who is able to increase his income somewhat above minimum level finds — as do Hollywood stars in our community — that a number of his more distant relatives offer to come and share his home with him. This increasing number of persons in wealthier families is bound to distort the results. Not many data are available on a per consumption unit basis. Khan, of Lucknow University,[1] has been able to do this for a number of civil servants' budgets in different cities, and also for steel workers at Jamshedpur; and in each case found an average income elasticity of 0·7.

A number of these relationships were also tested statistically to see whether the number of people in a family had any discernible influence upon consumption functions which had been measured per head. The only really outstanding figure was that for education in Japan, where the effect was *positive*. Unlike peasant families in Europe, which tend to spend less on education when they have several children to support, in the larger peasant families in Japan, apparently, the working members of the family are willing to make more effort than the smaller families to secure additional education for one of the family members. There were slight indications that the same thing was happening in India, though the results were hardly statistically significant.

Significant negative results were shown (i.e. capacity of large families to make *economies* in per head expenditure, not open to smaller families) for food consumption in both Japan and India, likewise for clothing in both countries.

A most important element in the economics of the life of the subsistence cultivator, which has received far too little study, is his housing. We may examine the available data in sq. m. (10·8 sq. ft.)/person.

For China, Buck found a much higher figure than might have been expected, of 8·5 sq. m./person (9·3 in the richer rice-growing region in the south, 7·4 in the north).

Surprisingly, almost the same figure (8·4) is found for Yugoslavia.[2] The figures range from 6–7 in Bosnia, Montenegro and

[1] N. A. Khan, Lucknow University, private communication.
[2] Vinski, International Association for Research in Income and Wealth, 1957 Conference.

Macedonia to 10·9 in Slovenia and 12·4 in Voivodina, the richest areas. The houses in Yugoslavia, however, are more substantially built.

Of the farm population of Jamaica[1] about one-third lives with less than 4 sq. m./person, half between 4 and 8.

Very low standards seem to prevail in India. In a small town[2] the median family had about 4·5 sq. m./person, a fifth of the families less than 2·3. In the rapidly growing city of Poona,[3] in 1953, the median was only 2·8, and nearly a third of all the people were below 2·3. In the worst districts of Singapore the average net dwelling space per person falls to 1·8 sq .m.;[4] and even worse crowding prevails in Hong Kong. What evidence we have indicates that crowding in mainland China is worse still. The table below shows the high income elasticity of demand for housing both among the peasant proprietors of the Punjab, and the Madras mill workers.

In the cold north China climate, however, consumption of clothing is substantial even at very low levels of income; conversely, Vietnam peasants, also living near the margin for subsistence, show a much lower income elasticity of demand for clothing since this community live in tropical south-east Asia. In eighteenth-century England income elasticity of demand was relatively high both for clothing and fuel; rent on the other hand was non-significant.

TABLE XXIX.   INCOME ELASTICITY OF DEMAND FOR NON-FOOD PRODUCTS

Country	Year	Clothing	Fuel	Housing	Taxes	Other
England	1795	1·84	1·35			
Vietnam	1938	0·65			0·86	
China (north) — Chinese	1914–18	2·56	0·90	0·45		3·69
China (north) — Manchu	1914–18	3·76	1·55	0·20		4·04
India — Punjab	1953–4	0·60		0·73		
India — Madras	1935–6	1·07	0·31	0·73		2·07
Japan — Kinki	1956	0·69		0·51		

Fraenkel[5] has found income elasticity of demand for clothing in Europe to range from 0·8 for high-income families to 1·6 for the

[1] D. Edwards, *An Economic Study of Small Farming in Jamaica*, 1961.
[2] Dhekney, *Hubli City*, Karnatak University, Dharwar.
[3] *Poona, A Resurvey*, Gokhale Institute, 1953.
[4] *Town and Country Planning*, November 1955, 'The Character of Cities', J. M. Fraser.
[5] Centraal Planbureau, The Hague, Overdrukken 62.

lowest. We need not, however, expect African or Asian income elasticities necessarily to be higher than 1·6 — after all, the poorer families in European countries suffer a considerable 'demonstration effect', causing them to desire to spend more on clothing than fairly they can. The relatively high income elasticity of demand for clothing in the Japanese sample in the above table is characteristic of a country in which consumption of clothing fibres has always tended to be above that of most Asian countries. Data from 1926–7 family expenditure studies showed an income elasticity of demand for clothing of 1·1.

When data are insufficient to give a significant estimate of income elasticity of demand, single measurements of inter-village differences may still be usefully compared with the chart. The unweighted mean of six villages in Thailand in 1930–1[1] showed that at an income level of 542 kg. wheat equivalent/person/year, the equivalent of 292 kg., or 54 per cent, was spent on food. Analysis of the available data suggests a higher level of food consumption, and income elasticity of demand for food higher than might have been expected, probably because Thailand includes areas in which communication is almost non-existent, market opportunities are poor, and incentives to exchange food for other goods lacking.

Overseas Chinese in Sarawak on smallholdings growing rubber, and employing no hired labour, appeared to be living at a lower level with an income of 283 kg. wheat equivalent/person/year, of which 231 kg., or 82 per cent, was spent on food.[2] On the other hand, Slater and Thomas[3] found in Vunagatla, an upland village in West Godavari District in India, that the average consumption of food in the village was no higher than 250 kg. wheat equivalent/person/year with an average income as high as 974 kg. The latter, however, included the earnings of toddy tappers, who derived a considerable income from this source.

Agricultural families in Bongouanou,[4] at an average income level of only 370 kg. wheat equivalent/person/year, and food consumption of 252 kg., still managed to save 7 per cent of their income. The relative cheapness of cassava, their staple food, is

[1] C. C. Zimmerman, *Siam Rural Economic Survey, 1930–31*.

[2] W. R. Geddes, *The Land Dayaks of Sarawak*, Colonial Research Study No. 14, 1954.

[3] University of Madras Economic Series, No. 1, *Some South Indian Villages*, ed. G. Slater, 1918; No. 4, *Some South Indian Villages, a Resurvey*, ed. P. J. Thomas, 1940.

[4] Enquête Nutrition, *Niveau de Vie, Subdivision de Bongouanou, 1955–56*. Territoire de la Cote d'Ivoire.

nevertheless somewhat offset by their dependence on high-priced meat and fish as sources of protein.

Beckett[1] found savings to be very high in his Akosoaso Village Survey — 154 kg. wheat equivalent/person/year out of an average income of 424 kg. Food consumption appeared to be near starvation level, however, ranging from 180 kg. to 210 kg., and savings may in fact have largely represented debt repayments.

We may now follow up these comparisons between families within a country with comparisons between countries. As agricultural productivity increases, this has two effects; first, everyone (agriculturists and non-agriculturists) has more to eat; secondly, an increasing proportion of the labour force can be diverted to non-agricultural activities. At first sight, one might indeed expect the whole of the increase to be used up in these two ways. This, however, ignores the country's needs for imports, which may be urgent. To obtain them, a country in the early stages of economic development must export food, except in so far as it can produce non-food agricultural products (cotton, tobacco, etc.); or oil, tin or other mineral products (in Japan's case also we include manufactures for export). These other products thus can 'substitute' for food in buying imports.

The remarkable abstemiousness of the Japanese appears as much in the international as in the inter-family comparisons: by setting resources free to buy imports, it has probably been of great value to them in accelerating their whole process of economic development.

The income elasticity of demand, we have seen, is the best measure to use when we are examining consumption of such objects as food and clothing, which are consumed in substantial quantities at every level of income. When, however, we are dealing with such an object as savings, which may be zero or even negative, or even if we are dealing with a commodity whose consumption is very small at the lower income levels, the method of logarithmic plotting becomes impracticable. When the income and consumption (or saving) are plotted on natural scales, and a straight line can be approximately drawn through the points, the slope of this line is defined as the 'marginal propensity to consume' (either for consumption or saving in the aggregate, or for consumption of individual commodities). This was the method of analysis which

---

[1] W. H. Beckett, *Akosoaso*, London School of Economics Monograph on Social Anthropology, No. 10.

was applied by Keynes. It is very important not to confuse *marginal propensity to consume* with *income elasticity of demand*. The marginal propensity to consume a commodity which plays a relatively small part in total consumption, for instance, must inevitably be small, even if its income elasticity of demand is very high. On the other hand, this method of analysis by marginal propensities is very useful, as Keynes found, to anyone who is trying to consider what the effects of an income change may be. It has been used for analysing both savings and imports.

As Keynes's idea got into circulation in the 1930s, many of his followers, particularly in the United States, set out to measure marginal propensity to save by simple comparisons, over a limited number of years, of income and savings data. This method gives estimates of the marginal propensity to save which, in fact, for a reason which we shall see in a moment, are far too high. Many of its practitioners were led by it to make quite unrealistic predictions of what was likely to happen in the 1940s, when wartime expenditure was reduced. Other economists, vaguely suspicious of this simple analysis of time series, set out to compare savings by families at widely different income levels.

The defect in both these methods of analysis was shown by Friedman.[1] People do not immediately adjust their expenditure, either upwards or downwards, in responses to changes in income. They tend to spend in accordance with what they regard as their probable average income. Friedman went on to show that, in fact, a weighted average of their incomes in recent past years, with weights exponentially diminishing as we go further back into the past, gives a good approximation to their estimate of their 'permanent' income, in accordance with which they control their spending.

It thus follows that any sudden rise or fall in income must of necessity lead temporarily to a much greater rise or fall in savings than that which is to be expected after people have had time to adjust their expenditure to any 'permanent' rise or fall of income. Conversely, where we use a set of data of family expenditures *at any given time* to estimate income elasticity, we are liable to include, in both the highest and the lowest income groups, families who have only recently entered these groups, and have not yet adjusted their expenditure upwards or downwards to them. In this way we tend to *underestimate* income elasticities of demand for commodities.

[1] M. Friedman, *The Theory of the Consumption Function*, Princeton, 1957.

There has not yet been much application of Friedman's principle to data on consumption and savings among subsistence cultivators, which data are scanty enough in any case. Some work has been done in Japan by Shinohara.[1] Marginal propensity to save among Japanese peasants, which appeared to be as high as 0·46 (i.e. 46 per cent of any increase in income saved) on a crude time-series analysis, was examined by inter-family comparisons in single years; for two years of good harvest (1951 and 1955) it averaged 0·38, and for a year of general bad harvest (1953) it averaged 0·31. This decline in the figure is as Friedman's theory would predict. Even if the true long period propensity to save on the part of Japanese peasants is only 0·25, this is still, however, a very high figure.

Japanese urban family expenditure data[2] show a marginal propensity to save of about 0·2, even at the lowest income levels, rising with ascending income, as might be expected. For the higher incomes, an income elasticity of demand for saving of 2·2 was concluded.

Some data for Indian industrial workers at Cawnpore[3] indicated a marginal propensity to save as high as 0·16.

Newman[4] made one of the few available studies of marginal propensity to import, based on family expenditure data, for a low-income economy. For the greater part of the people of Ceylon, up to an income level corresponding to 800 kg. grain/person/year, the marginal propensity to import was as high as 0·41, of which 0·28 represented imports of food. It was definitely only the wealthier people in Ceylon who had a higher marginal propensity to spend upon locally produced goods and services. It is rare to find a low-income country so dependent upon imports to meet the necessities of life as is Ceylon; but it is not unknown.

[1] Of Hitotsubashi University, privately communicated.
[2] *Proceedings of the International Institute of Statistics*, Tokyo Session, 1930, for 1926–7 results. *Monthly Labour Review*, Washington, October 1938, for 1936–7 results.
[3] Royal Commission on Indian Labour, 1928.
[4] *Studies in the Import Structure of Ceylon*, Ceylon Planning Secretariat, October 1958.

CHAPTER IX

Transport

I t cannot be emphasized too strongly that the first requisite for the improvement of the production of a subsistence economy is the provision of transport. Fertilizers, improved strains of seed, education and other objects are all of the greatest importance. But the need for transport is prior to all these. It follows from the nature of the case. If there is to be any improvement in an agriculture which at present only provides for subsistence, crops must be grown which can be sold. Selling implies transport to market. The methods of transport available to subsistence agricultural populations, as will be seen below, are so costly that produce only has to be carried a limited distance before most of its value, from the point of view of net returns from the sale, has gone.

The customary unit for measuring transport performance is a ton km., the carrying of one ton for a distance of a kilometre. As with production and consumption, we measure the cost of performing transport in terms of kg. grain equivalent/ton km. When, as in extreme cases, over 30 kg. of grain equivalent have to be expended in order to get one ton km. of transport performed, it is clear that transporting grain to market, even over a distance as short as 20 km., is economically out of the question — the costs of transport would have taken three-fifths of its value. In the eighteenth century Cantillon[1] took it for granted that food would not normally be transported more than 15 km. from its place of origin.

The cultivator may mitigate such a situation by growing for sale a crop which has a higher value per unit of weight, such as coffee (value of 1 kg. in grain units 5·6) or tobacco (value 8) — if his own skill, the productive possibilities of the soil and climate, and the availability of markets permit it. Thus in some of the more isolated mountainous regions of Macedonia the principal crop produced for sale is tobacco, because the burden of transport costs on it is relatively less; and many African cultivators have a preference for coffee for the same reason. It has been said in defence of the dwellers in the remote mountain regions of Kentucky, that their

[1] Spengler, *Journal of Political Economy*, 1954, pp. 289–93.

persistent tendency to produce 'moonshine', in face of all the efforts of excise officers, is explainable in terms of high transport costs in those regions, and the need to earn cash income and to produce for sale something which has a higher value per unit of weight than simple grain.

Transport in its simplest form — and there are many places where this is still the only possible form of transport — requires the direct carrying of goods by men or women in packs on their backs or, more usually in Africa or Asia, in loads balanced gracefully on their heads. Holmberg[1] has seen hunters in Bolivia return from the forest carrying up to 90 kg. game on their backs for a distance of 16 km. without exhibiting a great deal of fatigue. He found the average pack for a man or a woman to be about 30 kg. These Siriono hunters sometimes travel as many as 64 km. a day in their quest for game, and when nuclear families are away on hunting and gathering expeditions, men, women and children may walk 40 km. within a single day.

Even in the poorest and most primitive subsistence economy, a man must at least be well fed for the arduous task of carrying a heavy load all day — and also fed for the return journey. These requirements alone create a fairly high minimum cost, measured in kg. grain equivalent/ton km. In more advanced communities, as in those parts of southern Italy where some transport is still by porterage, where a man, however poor, nevertheless expects to be paid considerably more than the mere grain ration for a day's hard work, the grain equivalent of porterage costs becomes very high indeed.

The Chinese long ago invented the wheelbarrow (the Japanese shared this knowledge), which considerably reduced the cost of carrying heavy loads — though by no means everyone can afford to own one. (That they fitted their wheelbarrows with sails to catch the wind when it was favourable in order to help them on their journeys may be a fact, or merely an entertaining legend.) The simple but useful device of the wheelbarrow appears still to be unknown in many parts of the world. (Sidney Webb, travelling in Soviet Russia in the 1930s, supplemented his published account by remarking in private that the wheelbarrow and the mop appeared still to be unknown there, and that many heavy goods were still head-loaded, just as many floors were left uncleaned.)

[1] A. R. Holmberg, *Nomads of the Long Bow: the Siriono of Eastern Bolivia*, Smithsonian Institute of Social Anthropology, Publication No. 10, 1950.

When most transport in Japan was still by wheelbarrow along narrow paths[1] the maximum radius over which vegetables (less valuable per unit of weight than grain) could be supplied to towns was 12 km. With the advent of better roads and waggons this became 20 km., with motor trucks 40 km. These radii must not, however, be regarded as measuring the comparative costs of the different forms of transport. The ratio of motor transport cost to wheelbarrow cost is less than 12:40. Commerce became more competitive in the horse age, still more in the motor age, and consumers would not tolerate so large a proportion of the final cost of their purchases going to transport costs as they had at an earlier date.

In the newly settled areas in Mindanao,[2] where presumably roads are lacking, and transport has to be by porterage, the economic effect of high transport costs shows itself in the price of land. Near the markets a hectare of land sells at the equivalent of 3·3 tons of rough rice; at the equivalent of only 1·9 tons when distant 6 km. or more from market. If we assume that the buyers of land have on the average capitalized net income at ten years' purchase, this means that the transport disadvantage of the out-lying areas is, in effect, about one-tenth of the difference in land price, i.e. 140 kg. rice/ha./year, or 13 per cent of the gross product. If we take the average additional distance over which the rice has to be transported at 7 km., this implies a transport charge of 20 kg. rough rice, or 14 kg. milled rice/ton km., comparable with some of the highest figures given in the table. The Philippines is a comparatively high income country, and porters presumably have to be fairly well paid. However, the statement made by the Central Experiment Station, that in some cases the transportation agent charged as much as one unit of rice for every two units carried to market, cannot apparently be substantiated, except in a few isolated cases.

Conflicting statements have been made (see table for sources) regarding loads and distances covered by head porters. For Japan, the load was estimated at 45 kg. and the average journey 30 km./day. Gourou[3] gave 50 km./day at an average load of 40 kg. For Pakistan the figures are given as 20–40 kg. for head loads, 75–100 for shoulder baskets. Fei and Chang give for China the high

[1] Lockwood, writing in the Symposium by Kuznets and others, *Economic Growth — Brazil, India, Japan.*
[2] Philippines Central Experiment Station, Bulletin No. 1, 1957, p. 45.
[3] In his book, *The Tropical World*, 1961.

TABLE XXX. COMPARISON OF THE COST OF DIFFERENT METHODS OF TRANSPORT

Country or Region	Date	Length of journey (if specified) km.	Transport costs (original measure)	Grain equivalent used (if not wheat)	Transport cost expressed as kg. grain equivalent/ ton km.	Source
PORTERAGE						
Central America	1946		$0·88/ton mile		7·4	M
China	1929			millet	7·4	N
"	1930		0·71 yuan/ton mile	varied	4·5	A
"	1938			milled rice	2·0	P
East Africa	1953	11	10 shillings/ton mile		12·4	BB
France	1880		3·33 franc/ton km.		12·0	L
India and Pakistan	1937		7–12 pies/maund mile		8·2	B
Italy	1953		700 lire/ton km.		9·3	C
Kenya	1953		$1–1¼/ton mile		11·4	O
Northern Rhodesia	1930s				37·1	Q
East Pakistan	1958	25–30	4 annas/maund mile	milled rice	5·5	R
West Pakistan	1958		3 annas/maund mile		9·0	R
Turkey	1951		$1/ton mile		10·0	U
WHEELBARROW						
China	1929		0·30 yuan/ton mile		4·4	N
"	1930				1·9	A
BICYCLE						
Malaya	1958	140	$0·85–1/bag mile		34–40	X
PACK ANIMALS						
Camel: China	1929			millet	3·3	N
" Middle East	1930			varied	2·3	A
Pakistan	1880		0·87 francs/ton km.		1·7	L
Pakistan	1958		1⅛ annas/mile		4·5	R
Sudan	1937	140	£16·7/000 ton km.		2·1	AA
Donkey: China	1929		0·56 yuan/ton mile	millet	4·7	N
" East Africa	1930				3·5	A
Kenya	1953		9·5 shillings/ton mile		11·8	BB
Pakistan	1953				11·4	Q
	1958				6·0	R
Horse: Central America	1946				5·2	M
China	1929			millet	6·3	N
"	1930				3·4	A
"	1938				2·3	P
England	1655	11	8 pence/ton mile		4·1	T
"	1754	190	12 pence/ton mile	milled rice	6·2	T

	Date	No.	Cost	Commodity	Ref.	Value
India and Pakistan	1937		2·4–5·6 pies/maund mile		B	2·1–4·9
Italy	1953		440 lire/ton km.		C	5·9
Pakistan	1958				R	6·0
Turkey	1951		$1/ton mile		U	10·0
United States	1790		5½ shillings/ton mile		Y	7·5
Llama: Chile	1937		56 pesos/ton mile	millet	S	3·3
Mule: China	1929				N	3·4
„ China	1930				A	3·0
„ France	1880				L	3·1
CARTS AND WAGONS						
Australia	1795		20 pence/ton mile		I	2·8
„	1839	58	8 pence/ton mile		I	1·4
„	1854	225	24 pence/ton mile		I	3·4
„	1860		42–66 pence/ton mile		I	3·6–5·6
„ China	1929		24 pence/ton mile	millet	N	5·6
„	1930				A	2·6
England: long journeys	13th c.		3½ pence/ton mile		F	2·3
„ short journeys	13th c.		1 penny/ton mile		L	8·0
France	Estimate for 17th c. wagon design					2·3
France	1912		0·6 francs/ton km.		V	5·4
India (Nagpur-Mirzapore)	1848	800	£17.10.0/ton		G	2·2
India and Pakistan	1937	13			B	2·4
South India	1936	6			H	2·3
Italy	1953		270 lire/ton km.		C	3·3
„	1920				Q	1·8–5·5
Nigeria	1958		40 pence/ton mile		R	3·6
Pakistan urban areas	1958				KK	5·5
„ short journeys	1961				E	4·5
Roman Empire	3rd c. A.D.	Over 300	37 denarii/ton mile			7·5
Eastern Provinces	3rd c. A.D.	Under 300	20 denarii/1200 lb./mile			2·2
United States	1790–1818		21 cents/ton km.		W	3·2
„	1790–1818		13 cents/ton km.		Y	4·4
„	1800		15 cents/ton mile		Z	3·5
„	1887		20 cents/ton mile		K	1·6
TELEFERICHE						
Italy	1953		175 lire/ton km.		C	4·9
BOATS						
China	1928			millet	N	2·3
„	1930		0·14 yuan/ton mile		A	2·3
Egypt: canal	3rd c. A.D.		1 drachma/ton mile		D	0·9

Country or Region	Date	Length of journey (if specified) km.	Transport costs (original measure)	Grain equivalent used (if not wheat)	Transport cost expressed as kg. grain equivalent/ ton km.	Source
BOATS (Egypt)						
River Nile	3rd c. A.D.				0·3	D
England: Mersey and Irwell	17th c.		1 penny/ton mile (water route)		0·5	T
,, Thames	17th c.		2 pence/ton mile (water route)			
,, Thames	1790		2·4 pence/ton mile (water route)			
Pakistan	1958	5	1½ anna/maund mile	milled rice	2·1	R
,, short journey	1958	30		milled rice	0·7	R
,, long journey	1961	80	½ anna/maund mile	milled rice	1·9	KK
United States: canal	1810	450			0·6	KK
,, ,, New canal	1810	30			2·2	U
New Orleans-Louisville	1810				0·4	Y
,, ,,	1810				4·8	Y
,, ,, downstream	1810				0·9	Y
STEAMBOATS						
Central America	1946				0·6	M
China	1928			millet	4·1	N
,,	1930		0·08 yuan/ton mile		0·5	A
,, Nigeria	1955	850	2·34 pence/ton mile		0·4	CC
EARLY RAILWAY SYSTEMS						
Australia Wheat	1850s	250	6 pence/ton mile		1·4	J
,, Machinery	1870s	250	2 pence/ton mile		1·2	J
Central America	1870s		7 pence/ton mile		4·1	J
Chile	1946		8·3 cents/ton mile		1·2	M
China	1937		1·5 pesos/ton mile		0·1	S
China	1930		0·09 yuan/ton mile		0·57	A
England: Birmingham-Liverpool	1830s		4 pence/ton mile		1·3	T
,, London-Manchester	1830s		2·3 pence/ton mile		0·74	T
France	1830s		0·25 francs/ton km.		1·1	L
,,	1870s		0·06 francs/ton km.		0·22	L
Ghana	1955	160	3·65 pence/ton mile		0·61	CC
Nigeria	1955	760	2·73 pence/ton mile		0·45	CC
Tanganyika	1957		2·4 pence/ton mile		0·4	II

Borneo (assuming 50% average only)						
¾ ton jeeps	1960	10	43 cents/vehicle mile		3·3	JJ
" 3 ton trucks	1960	240	83 cents/vehicle mile		1·6	JJ
" 5 ton trucks	1960	240	96 cents/vehicle mile		1·1	JJ
Central America	1946				1·3	M
Ceylon: lowlands	1952		32 cents/ton mile	rough rice	0·34	GG
" lowlands	1952		23½ cents/ton mile	rough rice	0·25	GG
" highlands	1952		60 cents/ton mile	rough rice	0·64	GG
" highlands	1952		32½ cents/ton mile	rough rice	0·35	GG
Chile	1937		15 pesos/ton mile		1·1	S
China	1928				13·9	N
East Africa	1930		0·08 yuan/ton mile	millet	7·2	A
India (Delhi-Rajasthan)	1953		4½ shillings/ton mile		5·3	BB
lowest rate on agricultural goods	1960	30	26 NP/ton mile		0·65	HH
highest rate on industrial goods	1960	150	12 NP/ton mile		0·30	HH
Nigeria (Lagos and south)	1960		70 NP/ton mile		1·75	HH
" "	1960		20 NP/ton mile		0·50	HH
Pakistan (Punjab) average	1954	70	3·5 pence/ton mile		0·36	DD
"	1955		7·25 pence/ton mile		0·75	CC
Sudan	1950		3 pies/maund mile		1·25	FF
Uganda	1937				1·2	AA
" regular traffic	1950s	100–300	9·6 pence/ton mile		1·00	EE
	1950s		7·5 pence/ton mile		0·78	EE

Sources to Table on Comparison of the Cost of Different Methods of Transport

A Buck, *Land Utilization in China*, p. 354.
B *Report on Marketing of Jute in India*, 1940.
C Ugo Sorbi, Borgo e Mozzano, Instituto di Economia, University of Florence.
D Johnson, *Economic Survey of the Roman Empire*.
E Walbank, *Cambridge Economic History of Europe*.
F Postan, *Economic History of Europe*.
G Bourne, *Railways in India*.
H University of Madras, *Resurvey of some South Indian Villages, 1936–7*.
I Dunsdorf, *The Australian Wheat Growing Industry*.
J Shaun, *Economic History of Australia*.
K A.D. Welk, *Recent Economic Changes*, 1889.
L De Foville, *La Transformation des Moyens de Transport*.
M U.S. Department of Commerce, *International Reference Service*, 1949.
N Gamble, *Ting-Hsiem, A North China Rural Community*.
O *Land, Labour and Diet in Northern Rhodesia*.
P Fei and Chang, *Earthbound China*, p. 187.
Q Hance, *African Economic Development*.
R *Report on Marketing of Fresh Fruit in Pakistan*.
S Rudolph, *Geographical Review*, September 1952.
T Jackman, *Development of Transport in Modern England*, 1916.
U Renshaw, *University of Chicago Journal of Business*, October 1960.

V Bernard, *La Progrès Agricole*.
W Jasny, *Wheat Studies* (Stanford), March 1944.
X Wilson, *Economics of Padi Production in Northern Malaya*, Malayan Ministry of Agriculture.
Y Carnegie Institute, *History of Transport in U.S. before 1860*, 1917.
Z Cochran and Millar, *The Age of Enterprise*.
AA Tothill, *Agriculture in the Sudan*, Oxford University Press, 1948.
BB East African Royal Commission, 1953–55.
CC United Africa Company, *Statistical and Economic Review*, March 1957.
DD Hawkins, Colonial Office Research Study No. 32.
EE Hawkins, *Road Transport in Nigeria*.
FF Yasin, Punjab Board of Economic Enquiry, Bulletin No. 114.
GG International Bank, *Economic Development of Ceylon*.
HH National Council of Applied Economic Research, New Dehli Occasional Paper No. 2.
II International Bank, *Economic Development of Tanganyika*.
JJ Report on Transport Requirements in the Light of Economic Developments in North Borneo, Colonial Office 1960.
KK Report on the Marketing of Jute in East Pakistan, University of Dacca.

Median Transport Cost expressed as
Kg. Grain Equivalent/Ton Km.

Porterage	9·0
Pack animals:	
Camel	2·3
Llama	3·3
Mule	3·1
Donkey	6·0
Horse	5·9
Wheelbarrow	3·1
Carts and wagons	3·4
Boats	0·9
Steamboats	0·6
Early railway systems	0·7
Motor vehicles	1·0
Teleferiche (Italy)	2·3

figure of a 59 kg. load, and also imply that distances up to 50 km. may be covered daily. However, even the strongest men can only do such work for twelve days a month, and receive two or three times the wages of an ordinary agricultural worker. Another estimate for China[1] gives 47 kg. carried for 32 km./day. The Rhodesian figures, on the other hand, are for only 23 kg. carried 25–30 km. These lower standards of effort, and higher real wages, explain the very high cost. When jute is head-loaded in India and Pakistan, the average load is stated to be about 40 kg.

There are indications that these very heavy loads call for a quite disproportionate effort. Phillips[2] found that for head-load carrying total energy expenditure increases linearly with the weight of head load carried up to a certain optimum level, which would appear to be at 20 kg., and that any further increase in the weight of head loads leads to a disproportionate increase in energy cost.

In assessing the physiologically optimum head load, three factors should be taken into account: (a) the distance of carry; (b) the rate of carry; and (c) the period of rest. He argues that a head load of 20 kg. would be considered the upper limit if the carrier were walking for some time without rest, but that a load of 30 or 35 kg. would not be excessive, and would ensure a high degree of efficiency, provided that the distance of carry was short, or that the carrier returned unloaded (equivalent to a normal rest period). This, he notes, is in fact the custom in Africa. For long marches a

[1] Winfield, *China, the Land and the People*, 1948.
[2] P. G. Phillips, 'The Metabolic Cost of Common West African Agricultural Activities', *Journal of Tropical Medicine and Hygiene*, London, 1954, Vol. 57, No. 12.

carrier's load rarely exceeds 22 kg., and is normally not more than 14 kg., but in the tin mines, where the carries are short, the load is often more than 27 kg.; and in agricultural centres, sacks of groundnuts or cocoa beans weighing up to 100 kg. are often humped short distances. An important point is the position of the centre of gravity of the load relative to that of the body, which favours the carriage of loads on the head, since complete control and a stable centre of gravity is maintained throughout.

Another form of improved transport, without the use of animal power, is transport by bicycle, which is widespread in Africa. Malayan data show costs to be very high. These high figures are confirmed by other observers. Again however, Malaya is a relatively high-wage country.

For the very poor countries, pack animals do not represent any great saving over human porterage — the cost of maintaining the animal is high, in relation to the price of labour. The horse is the most expensive animal to maintain, and costs correspondingly high. The rise in pack-horse costs in England between the seventeenth and eighteenth centuries, shown in the table, is probably explainable in terms of rising real wages.

Direct comparisons of the cost of pack-horse and human transport were made in the Chinese village study by Fei and Chang, and the horse found to be more costly. The average pack horse only carried 90 kg., as against the man's 60 kg., and travels about half as fast again, requires one day's rest in five, and in this particular district only works nine months of the year because of the climate. With the work it did, and the keep it received, the average life of a pack horse was found to be only about one year. In East Africa, comparatively high rates of wages show themselves in the very high charges for transport both by porter and by pack donkey.

A number of data are available for the cost of cart and wagon transport, for a great variety of times and places. The costs of long journeys seem to have been much higher than of short journeys, probably owing to the greater risk of having to return without a load. Nearly all the data referred to ox wagons; it was not until the nineteenth century, and then only in some countries, that the use of the horse wagon became widespread. De Foville's figures for France show that improvements in wagon design played an important part in reducing costs; these in their turn are only made possible by an improvement in roads. However, the Indian report on the marketing of jute indicated that transport costs by ox wagon on metalled roads were no lower than on unmetalled.

In Australia, the great rise in money costs in 1854 (the rise in real costs was less) was the consequence of the Gold Rush. The rates shown prevailed only in the summer, when the roads in Victoria were dry. In winter, when the roads were muddy, and the oxen needed for ploughing, rates might be five times as high. After the Gold Rush, real costs settled down at a considerably higher figure, than before the Gold Rush owing to higher real wages.

A similar rise in the United States is noticeable. In the decades just before the arrival of motor transport, it was reckoned in the United States that it was quite uneconomic for anyone much more than 100 km. from the railway to attempt to produce wheat. This would indeed be the case, if transport costs were of the order of magnitude of $3\frac{1}{2}$ kg. wheat/ton km., which transport costs would, in effect, use up a third of the crop in transporting it to the railway. In Australia, the economic limit was generally adjudged at a shorter distance. The consequence, in both countries, was a close network of railway branches (many of which have since been abandoned, but clearly discernible on contemporary maps) demarcating the 'wheat belt'.

Renshaw describes the average Turkish ox cart as carrying a quarter ton and only travelling 8 km./day. The University of Madras however reports wagons carrying over half a ton for short distances.

In England, between the 1780s and the 1830s, there was a substantial reduction in real transport costs, which Jackman attributes to the macadamizing of the roads. On routes where rail competition was beginning to make itself felt in the 1830s, he states that road charges were reduced to 5d./ton mile.

Transport costs can be substantially reduced by using boats. The high cost of land transport explains why so many ancient and mediaeval cities were built on the sea or on navigable rivers. The Aztecs, whose only land transport was by head-loading, built their capital city by a large lake, thereby facilitating the collecting of supplies over a greater distance than would have been possible otherwise.

We find rather similar real costs of water transport prevailing in ancient Rome and Egypt, in seventeenth-century England, and in modern China. On the River Nile, boats of $5\frac{1}{2}$ tons capacity were used, which greatly reduced costs, as compared with smaller boats, but larger boats were used in Roman sea transport. Jasny estimated that Roman sea transport costs, expressed as wheat equivalent/ton km., were only about three times those of modern shipping. Relative to agricultural and industrial production costs, sea transport was cheap in the ancient world, and the carriage of goods over comparatively long distances was therefore quite economic.

In England, navigation on the Mersey and Irwell was fairly straightforward, but the Thames was considerably obstructed by weirs. Moreover the river journey from London to Oxford was 2·1 times the length of the road journey. The figures in the table are per river mile, and upstream; downstream rates were about 25 per cent lower. On the canals, the water routes also generally worked out at almost twice the length of the road routes. Costs by canal were comparable with those on the Thames, because the locks imposed considerable costs and delays.

The figures for United States water transport, on the other hand, are computed per km. of *direct* route.

As wages rose and wagon transport became more expensive, the economic advantages of the canals and rivers, with the possibility of putting a much greater load under the charge of one man (at the cost of much greater capital outlay) became more apparent. The use of steam boats brought much further advantage. In the United States they were already in use in the 1820s; and the whole development of the Continent would have been far slower without them. Where rivers and canals are comparatively broad and unobstructed, they have been able to remain in active competition with railways as a means of transport to this day.

As might have been expected, costs on the early railway systems were high, and in Australia were still high in the 1870s. But as the techniques of railway operations improved, costs could be brought down, even on the smaller and more isolated systems.

When goods transport by road motor vehicle first made its appearance, for example in China, its costs were inordinately high. In the 1920s road motor transport was still a comparatively high cost form of transport in Europe, used only for fairly short distances to save the extra loading and unloading required for a railway journey. In recent years it has still been very costly in some of the remoter parts of East Africa (although the very high figure quoted by the Royal Commission appears to be exaggerated). Naturally, the costs go down as the roads improve — see for instance the difference between the northern Nigerian average, and

M

the costs for the more developed southern regions. In areas with good roads, such as Ceylon and the Delhi region in India, costs have been brought right down, and are now comparable with those of the railways. Railway charges have to be much lower than road charges if they are to offset road transport's greater quickness and convenience, and its avoidance of double handling.

What can be the economic effects of a transport cost of the order of 1·1 kg. grain equivalent/ton km. is illustrated in a striking point made by Gourou.[1] At Gao on the Upper Niger (not far from the better known Timbuktu), about 1250 km. from the coast in a direct line, cement costs six times its price on the coast. At Kano in Northern Nigeria on the other hand, although the distance from the coast is over 1100 km., the price of cement is only raised to 1·6 times its price on the coast (2·5 times its f.o.b. price in Britain), through the provision of a good road and railway system.

The costs and advantages of improving roads have been studied in the North-west Frontier Province of Pakistan,[2] and by Sargent.[3] Data are also given by Hawkins[4] and Pedler.[5]

Sargent ascertains the costs of a 5-ton vehicle at 17 pence/ vehicle km. in Borneo, and estimates that a third of these costs could be saved by the use of bituminized roads as compared with 'improved earth'. Hawkins is considering cheaper transport in Africa, at costs which we may assume at 12 pence/vehicle km. for a 5-ton vehicle, of which he considers only 15 per cent could be saved by providing a bituminized surface as compared with gravel (two-fifths of this saving is on the depreciation of the vehicle). An alternative estimate, however,[6] makes the relative saving twice as high. In West Africa, where road transport costs in general are considerably lower, Pedler puts the savings from bituminization at 18 per cent. Conversion from an unmade road to an 'earth track capable of carrying 15 ton lorries', according to Pedler, saved 25 per cent of transport costs.

---

[1] Annuaire de Cellege de France, 1959–60, p. 307.
[2] Provincial Government Offices, private communication. In 1952, at the time of the enquiry, the Province had 2670 km. of pack tracks, 1450 km. of motorable earth roads, 2580 km. of gravelled roads, and 2600 km. of metalled or tarred roads. The prices quoted were converted at the old exchange rates of 13·3 rupees/£ and then raised 25 per cent to bring them up to date.
[3] Report on Transport Requirements in the Light of Economic Developments in North Borneo, 1960. Exchange converted at $8·4 Borneo/£.
[4] E. K. Hawkins, Road Transport in Nigeria, O.U.P., 1958.
[5] F. J. Pedler, Economic Geography of West Africa, London, 1955.
[6] R. S. Millard, 'Road Development in the Overseas Territories', Journal of the Royal Society of Arts, Vol. 107, p. 5032, March 1959.

Reviewing the available evidence, Hawkins suggests that when traffic reaches 300 vehicles/day, bituminization becomes worth while.

Each km. of road built, Sargent estimates, has the effect of opening some 60 ha. of new agricultural land. He estimates further that each pound spent on road building has the effect of permanently raising gross agricultural production in Borneo by as much as £4/year. This result, however, he points out, must not be taken at its face value. It is true that road building attracts new settlers into an area, who immediately become productive; but population and labour are scarce factors in Borneo, and the growth of production following upon the construction of a new road may be at the expense of production elsewhere.

TABLE XXXI. ESTIMATES OF COST OF ROADS

Construction Costs

	Pakistan	Borneo £/km.	East Africa[1]	Maintenance Costs: Borneo £/km./year
Original earth road or jeep track	1750	1080	620	
Do. in mountain country	5850			
Gravelled roads[a]	2040	2170	2490	90
Metalled roads[a]	4040	5800 }	} 7460	140
Additional costs for bituminizing metalled road	1930[c]	2900 }		150[b]

[a] Specified as 3·65 metres width in Pakistan.
[b] Hawkins estimates 115.
[c] £440 each for two coats of tar surfacing plus £1050 for a carpet of 3·8 cm. (half that cost if carpet 2·5 cm.). The above however are all for a road of 3·65 m. width — well trafficked bituminous roads should be widened to 6 m. (20 feet).

The essential role of transport is to permit the exchange of goods between the cultivators and urban centres, whereby it becomes possible (and without which it is impossible) for the economic position of the cultivator to rise above subsistence level, consuming locally grown food and simple handicrafts produced in his own village, and practically nothing else; while in the absence of transport towns could not exist at all.

[1] E. K. Hawkins, *Roads and Road Transport in an Underdeveloped Country*, A case study of Uganda, 1962, p. 203.

Before we consider the growth of towns, and their dependence upon transport, we should bear in mind certain effects of the lack of transport on the agricultural sector itself. The extraordinary differences between villages in the same region found by Buck in China, with some villages starving and others with an obvious surplus of food, can only be explained in terms of an almost complete lack of transport. In Thailand, where transport is very inadequate, Zimmerman[1] found that the fertile delta region of the Menam Plain suffered violent fluctuations in the local price of rice, which threatened to disrupt the whole social economy, which arose from the fact that certain areas almost entirely lacked normal marketing and transport facilities. There appeared to be many regions in Thailand, at present almost uninhabited, which could be made very productive; others, such as the fertile alluvial soil region in central Thailand, are already very densely populated. A transfer of labour from one region to the other would benefit everybody; but this cannot be considered till transport has been improved. Within a single village in West Bengal[2] there was evidence that, as access to markets improved, a larger proportion of the crop was offered for sale, even by the poor cultivators. The comparatively low income elasticity of demand of Japanese cultivators for the food which they had produced themselves, and the correspondingly high income elasticity of demand for other goods, could not have been possible except in a country with good transport and communications.

It is clear that the origin of urban settlements depends upon transport; not only their food, but also their fuel and building materials, constituting loads of similar orders of magnitude, have to be brought from a distance. The cities established by the Aztecs, the Incas and the Maya, who had no means of transport except head-loading, are the exception which proves the rule. They appear to have required a very authoritative form of society, and the imposition of heavy duties upon all able-bodied men, just in the performance of transport; and we have Gourou's opinion that the Maya civilization broke down through soil exhaustion, consequent upon the attempt to go on growing maize without fertilizers in the areas immediately adjacent to their cities, presumably because they could not face the prospects of having to transport it from a distance.

---

[1] C. C. Zimmerman, *Siam Rural Economic Survey, 1930–31*.
[2] Mandal, 'The Marketable Surplus of Anan Paddy in East Indian Villages', *Indian Journal of Agricultural Economics*, January–March 1961, p. 51.

The first towns were (and we can say of some parts of the world to-day, still are) military strongholds, seats of kings or administrators, and religious centres. The performers of these functions required an inflow of substantial quantities of food, fuel and building materials. Rather later, towns have developed their commercial functions, calling also for an outward movement of certain types of goods. Nevertheless, the early urban civilizations tended to grow up, not only where good sea and river transport was available, but also on arid (and therefore fertile) land where perennially high yields could be obtained by irrigation (e.g. Jericho, Egypt, Iraq and the Indus valley).

One of the great technical improvements of the classical world was in the building of ships, though it did not shine in land transport. In mediaeval Europe the techniques of land transport, and also of ploughing, were potentially considerably improved by the invention of the horse collar (whose date is uncertain); though in fact most subsistence cultivators were too poor to keep horses, and oxen with their heavy yokes continued to be used both for ploughing and for transport until comparatively recent times. But the improvements in shipbuilding made possible the transport over considerable distances, not only of goods whose value was high in relation to their weight, such as hides, wool and metals, but also of grain, wine and timber. But away from waterways the average village still depended upon high-cost land transport, could not therefore in fact sell any substantial proportion of its agricultural product, and had to rely upon its own handicrafts for most of its non-agricultural requirements.

This examination of the economics of mediaeval Europe is more than an academic exercise. If for the concept of waterways we substitute that of waterways plus a limited number of lines of modern rail and road transport, the economy of many Asian and African villages to-day, if they are more than a few miles removed from railways and main roads, remains very similar to that of the more backward villages of mediaeval Europe.

It was not until the mid-eighteenth century in western Europe that a road system as good as that of the Roman Empire was again in use. This is illustrated in an interesting manner by the fact that horse-drawn sleeping cars were in widespread use in the third century A.D. Apparently the Very Important Persons of those days travelled with a speed and comfort not subsequently equalled till a sleeping car was built for Napoleon, and he probably had to put up with much rougher roads. This improvement in roads made possible the replacement of pack horses by wagons, with consequent reduction of goods transport costs.

While efficient transport is a condition necessary for the growth of cities, we must not assume that it alone is sufficient. There is also an implicit political condition, which is of more fundamental importance. The complex economic network necessary to support a city cannot be constructed except under conditions of political stability and security. The cultivator, trader, and craftsman cannot safely enter into a system of mutual economic dependence until they can trust the rulers of the city to protect them alike from invasion from without and disturbances from within. Recurring wars and revolutions create an atmosphere of insecurity which eventually makes men unwilling to take the risks involved in any form of economic specialization. Society then slips back into a simpler form of household economy or, at best, a village economy, as it did in Europe at the break-up of the Roman Empire — and on many other occasions in history.

In England, even in the days of pack-horse transport, small manufacturing centres had sprung up in Birmingham and Sheffield, from which high valued metal goods were distributed by pack horse. But generally speaking manufacture, as we understand the word, namely the continuous processing of goods for distribution to a large market, is absolutely dependent upon reasonably cheap transport.

A transport economy depending primarily upon wagons travelling along improved roads, as in the later eighteenth century, made possible the growth of quite large cities. But their growth was certainly held in check by transport considerations. From information given by Arthur Young, it is possible to draw contours showing steadily rising prices as London was approached. This in turn necessitated considerably high money wages (though probably not real wages) in London than elsewhere; which factor in turn checked the growth of manufactures there.

Railway transport (mechanical road transport in the modern world) brings about the greatest *relative* reduction in the costs of transport of heavy and bulky goods. Its effects upon agriculture are more immediate than upon industry; it becomes feasible to transport away from the producing areas even comparatively low-valued crops. From the proceeds of these sales the cultivator is able to buy numerous cheap manufactured goods, and to dispense with the high-priced products produced by the village weavers and other craftsmen, who are thus forced to seek urban employment, or remain persistently underemployed. We can see this tragic but unavoidable process occurring in England about the 1830s, in India about fifty years later, as the railways spread, and we can see it happening in some parts of the world now.

Of equal importance, however, is the fact that, while subsistence agriculture had to produce all the local requirements of food and fibre, once modern transport has been introduced geographical specialization of agriculture rapidly follows, with consequent further increases in productivity.

CHAPTER X

Trade, Aid and Development

As a subsistence economy develops, (a) it consumes more of its own food, (b) it is able to divert a gradually increasing proportion of its labour force to non-agricultural tasks, and (c) it trades more with the rest of the world.

Data for individual villages illustrating these principles are few. In the poorest communities we expect the major part of the working time to be devoted to agriculture. Precise information is, however, hard to obtain, and the following analysis by Sol Tax appears to be unique.[1]

TABLE XXXII. USE OF WORKING DAY IN AN INDIAN VILLAGE IN GUATEMALA

	Men	Women	Children over 14
Time occupied, hours/day	10·48	9·03	6·63
Of which time devoted to:			
marketing	0·55	0·88	0·78
housework and production of goods for own use	0·38	4·98	2·72
Time available for 'economic' activities, hours/day	9·55	3·17	3·13
Percentage distribution of above:			
agriculture	91·0	91·0	96·5
production of other goods and services for sale	2·9	8·0	3·5
governmental and public duties	6·1	1·0	—

It is not however made clear whether this information was collected (as it appears to have been) in the busy agricultural season, and whether there was a slack season, with more time for leisure, and for non-agricultural pursuits.

Beckett found in a village in Ghana in the 1930s,[2] omitting the unoccupied, and those working away from the village, that 15 per cent of the men were fully occupied in non-agricultural occupa-

[1] S. Tax, *Penny Capitalism, a Guatemalan Indian Economy*, Smithsonian Institution of Social Anthropology, Publication No. 16, Washington, 1953.

[2] *Akosoaso*, London School of Economics Monograph on Social Anthropology, No. 10.

tions, and another 15 per cent in mixed occupations; for the women, the respective figures were 9 and 8 per cent.

Taking the nation as a unit, we have a substantial quantity of data, of production, of the numbers engaged in non-agricultural activities, and of imports and exports. From now until the end of this book, therefore, our analysis will be made solely on national data.

In China, Buck recorded that 20 per cent of the men had occupations other than agriculture, and that a further 14 per cent, though predominantly agricultural, also followed some other activities. A total of $83\frac{1}{2}$ per cent of the working population occupied in agriculture, forestry and fishing was shown for Japan in 1872.[1] The Census for Thailand showed 84 per cent occupied in agriculture in 1929. For Nicaragua it was 84 per cent in 1920 and 78 per cent in 1940, for Bulgaria 81 per cent in 1910 and 78 per cent in 1934. There may, it is true, be a certain ambiguity in these figures, with the inclusion in agriculture of some who have part-time activities elsewhere.

The time has not yet come for the preparation of a full economic model, or system of equations, to describe the inter-relationship between these phenomena. The rise in food consumption depends upon the income elasticity of demand for food which, we have seen, is very variable between different times and communities, and itself appears to depend upon the availability, and price, of other goods. We should expect increasing productivity to increase demand for imports; but it does not do so in a manner precisely predictable. The amount imported may be influenced by the exchange rate and by the terms of trade, for there are also certain possibilities of substitution between imports and home-produced goods. Moreover, as we shall see below, some countries, at a given level of real income per head, require considerably more imports than others.

Nor do we yet know how relative preferences for goods and leisure are affected by rise in productivity. We may turn back to what we have called 'Mujumdar's relationship', showing how in India the wealthier cultivators' families prefer to work a compara-tively low number of hours/year, even when they are able to buy all the land that they want. It is very possible that a leisure preference relationship similar to that for India prevails in the present-day western world, similarly shaped, and with similar maximum and

[1] Kimura, *Annals of the Hitotsubashi University*, April 1956.

minimum hours, but shifted extensively to the right along the income scale, with the wealthiest company directors working about 1500 hours/year in all, and heads of poor families working overtime to bring their year up to 2500 hours.

One or two useful empirical relationships between these variables have however been discovered, which enable us to carry the analysis a stage further.

Following de Vries, stages of economic development were first measured by computing grain equivalents of agricultural (including non-food) production/population. In the least-developed communities, the ratio of agricultural population to total population is high, and can be assumed not to vary significantly. But as we advance up the income scale, the proportion of agricultural population may be reduced considerably. Here the figure (grain equivalent of all agricultural production/agricultural population) appears more suitable for our purpose.

In a preliminary analysis, in which an attempt was made to relate the above variable to imports (also expressed in grain equivalents/population) certain discrepancies were noticed in countries having large exports of minerals or forest products. It became clear that such exports can directly 'substitute' for agricultural products in purchasing required imports, thus setting more of the agricultural production free to feed industrial workers in the country, or for other purposes. The same applies to the small quantities of manufactured exports which some of these countries produce (though in measuring these we should exclude their raw-material content, otherwise we may count it twice). These non-agricultural exports are therefore converted to grain equivalents on the basis of current world prices, and added to agricultural production to give what is best defined as 'exportable product' (though most of the food produced is not in fact exported). The production of minerals, forest products and manufactures for internal use cannot at this stage be measured, and has to be left out of the calculation.

While census data for countries with a large proportion of subsistence agriculturists generally give precise information of the numbers actually at work in non-agricultural occupations, they often show for the agricultural community only the total numbers supported by agriculture, without any very clear distinction between workers and dependants — which would in any case be very difficult to obtain, in view of the large amount of part-time

TABLE XXXIII. NON-AGRICULTURAL EXPORTS EXPRESSED IN KG. ECONOMIC WHEAT EQUIVALENT/PERSON/YEAR

	Timber and Forest Products	Minerals	Manufactured Goods
North Africa			
Algeria	—	59	44
Egypt	—	11	28
Ethiopia	—	—	1
Libya	—	6	9
Morocco	4	185	7
Sudan	—	—	4
Tunisia	5	137	51
Rest of Africa			
Angola	10	66	33
Cameroun	22	45	—
Congo and Ruanda Urundi	4	170	7
Former French Equatorial Africa	110	27	—
Former French West Africa (excl. Guinea)	14	—	—
Ghana	95	155	4
Guinea	—	20	—
Kenya	3	16	3
Liberia	—	276	—
Nigeria and British Cameroons	6	7	2
Rhodesia and Nyasaland	—	468	35
South Africa	23	354	271
Tanganyika	5	22	4
Togo	—	—	—
Near East			
Iran	—	226	14
Iraq	—	1189	—
Israel	—	11	543
Jordan	—	27	4
Lebanon	—	16	103
Syria	—	—	79
Turkey	1	17	4
Far East			
Burma	8	7	5
Ceylon	—	1	4
India	—	5	18
Indonesia	—	55	1

	Timber and Forest Products	Minerals	Manufactured Goods
Japan	4	12	407
Malaya	15	274	47
Pakistan	—	—	5
Philippines	46	33	19
South Korea	—	5	3
Taiwan	—	1	17
Thailand	10	10	9
Latin America			
Bolivia	—	270	—
Brazil	12	23	5
Chile	13	645	24
Colombia	—	84	6
Costa Rica	—	—	29
Cuba	—	64	43
Dominican Republic	2	4	6
Ecuador	6	3	6
El Salvador	—	1	27
Guatemala	4	—	—
Haiti	—	—	5
Honduras	54	24	5
Mexico	1	83	41
Nicaragua	33	—	3
Panama	—	—	—
Paraguay	118	—	18
Peru	—	182	—
Venezuela	—	5227	—

Source: U.N. Yearbook of International Trade Statistics, 1960.

work done by women and children. The best method of measuring the growth of non-agricultural occupations therefore, in the first instance, is to measure the number of non-agricultural workers as a percentage of the total population. We then assume that each non-agricultural worker has on the average 1·5 dependants (something like this ratio is found in nearly all countries for which we have information). By deducting the non-agricultural workers and their presumed dependants from the total population, we are left with an estimate of 'agricultural population'. We can then use this as a divisor for figures of 'exportable product'.

As is seen from the diagram below, there is a reasonably good relationship, over a considerable range of productivity, between the number of non-agricultural workers as a proportion of the total population, and the logarithm of exportable product per head of agricultural population.

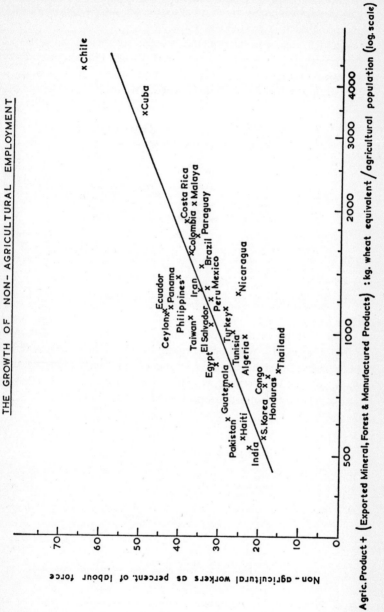

CHART XVI.

THE GROWTH OF NON-AGRICULTURAL EMPLOYMENT

Non-agricultural workers as percent of labour force

Agric. Product + (Exported Mineral, Forest & Manufactured Products) : kg. wheat equivalent / agricultural population (log. scale)

x Chile

x Cuba

x Costa Rica
x Colombia x Malaya
x Brazil Paraguay

Ceylon x Ecuador
x Panama
Philippines x
Taiwan x Iran
El Salvador x Peru Mexico
Egypt x Turkey x
Tunisia x
Algeria x

x Nicaragua

Pakistan x Guatemala
x Haiti
India x S. Korea Congo
Honduras x Thailand

The individual data for countries here shown were obtained from the tables, previously given, of agricultural output and of the other components of 'exportable product'.

Besides these comparisons for a large number of countries at a single date, it is interesting also to examine data for single countries at various stages of development. Data for certain periods for Japan, Soviet Russia and France were as follows.

TABLE XXXIV. JAPAN: GROWTH OF NON-AGRICULTURAL EMPLOYMENT

Year	Food production (incl. fish)	Non-food agricultural production	Non-agricultural exports (manufactures less raw material content)	Total 'exportable product' (sum of 3 previous cols.)	Non-agricultural workers as % of total population	Food consumption kg. wheat equivalent/ year/head of total population
			kg. wheat equivalent/year/head of agricultural population			
1872				(450)	7·7	
1885–9	469	45	4	518	12·6	310
1895–9	630	58	22	710	16·2	361
1905–9	785	71	54	910	18·6	387
1910–14	971	85	73	1129	19·8	442
1920–4	1380	127	210	1717	21·4	531
1925–9	1537	180	263	1980	21·3	556
1934–8	1759	212	522	2493	23·0	529

Sources: W. W. Lockwood, *The Economic Development of Japan,* O.U.P., 1955; League of Nations, *Industrialization and Foreign Trade,* 1945.

The data on food consumption are not directly relevant to the present issue. But we should remind ourselves of what has already been stated, that it was the low-income elasticity of demand for food, as income increased, which enabled Japan to divert labour to industry, and to import equipment, to so great an extent.

TABLE XXXV. SOVIET UNION: GROWTH OF NON-AGRICULTURAL EMPLOYMENT

Year	Population m.	Non-agricultural wage and salary workers (incl. Forces) m.	Non-agricultural wage and salary workers as % of population	Agricultural production bill. kg. wheat equivalent	Agricultural population[a] m.	Agricultural production per head of agricultural population kg. wheat equivalent
1913	139·3	9·9	7·1	147·2	114·5	1289
1926	147	9·1	6·2	141·3	124·6	1135
1939	170·6	28·5	16·7	168·9	113·6	1488
1956	200	48·3	24·1	229·9	103·4	2220

[a] Assuming 1½ dependents/worker to 1926, 1 subsequently.
Source: The Real Product of the Soviet Union, U.S. Senate publication, 1961.

N.B. Considerable boundary changes took place in 1918-21 and 1940-5. Figures for 1913 refer to 1921-40 boundaries; for 1956 refer to contemporary boundaries.

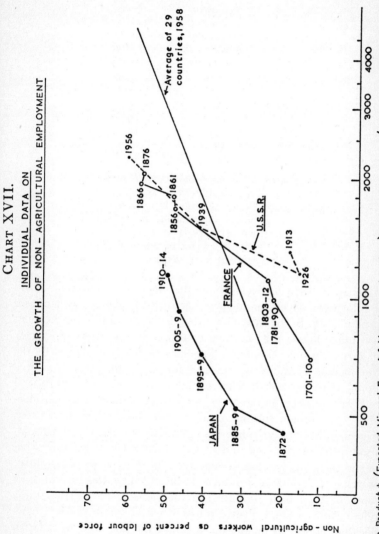

CHART XVII.

INDIVIDUAL DATA ON

THE GROWTH OF NON-AGRICULTURAL EMPLOYMENT

Average of 29 countries, 1958

U.S.S.R.

FRANCE

JAPAN

1956
1876
1866
1861
1856
1939
1913
1926
1910-14
1905-9
1895-9
1885-9
1872
1803-12
1781-90
1701-10

Non-agricultural workers as percent of labour force

70
60
50
40
30
20
10
0

Agric. Product + (Exported Mineral, Forest & Manufactured Products): kg. wheat equivalent/agricultural population (log. scale)

500
1000
2000
3000
4000

TABLE XXXVI.   FRANCE: GROWTH OF NON-
AGRICULTURAL EMPLOYMENT

Year	Productivity kg. wheat equivalent per head of agricultural population	Non-agricultural workers as % of total population
1701–10	680	4–6
1781–90	976	8·8
1803–12	1104	9·2
1856	1656	19·1
1861	1772	19·3
1866	1912	22·6
1876	2024	22·3

Source: Toutain, *Cahiers d'ISEA*, No.
115, Tables 141 and 145 (1
Franc of 1905–14 purchasing
power equivalent to 4 kg.
wheat). *Etudes et Conjoncture*,
May 1953 (for non-agricultural
workers from 1856).

Japan in 1872 had just about the amount of non-agricultural
employment which might have been predicted from agricultural
productivity. In the subsequent decades however this employment
was much higher than in other countries at a corresponding stage
of agricultural development. This may be partly explained by the
low income elasticity of demand for food, already commented
upon, partly perhaps by relatively low consumption of imports.

Russia in 1913, on the other hand, was a country with considerably *less* non-agricultural employment than might have been
expected from its agricultural productivity. By 1926, both agricultural productivity and industrial employment were somewhat
below their 1913 levels. It may have been that the comparative
scarcity of industrial products induced cultivators to consume
more of their own produce. In the subsequent decades these
relationships were violently transformed; though Soviet Russia
does not appear to be any more 'above the line' now than Japan
has been.

Eighteenth- and early nineteenth-century France also shows
industrial employment 'below the line'; though even in the 1780s
France was not so far below as Russia in 1913 or 1926. Lack of

transport and communication, in each case, must be regarded as the principal cause.

The violent upward shift of the relationship in Russia in the 1930s was brought about by the forcible 'collectivization' of farming. Japan also showed a strong upward shift in the 1870s, brought about in this case by the imposition of a very severe land tax. In France, on the other hand, a similar climb, though less rapid, took place in the ordinary course of commercial development. Some say that the widespread industrialization of any country can only be brought about by an impulse of somewhat violent and, from the point of view of those living at the time, unpleasant character. If we have to choose between a land tax and compulsory collectivization, a land tax is probably the lesser evil. It is no use, however, attempting to apply it in those parts of Africa where population densities are so low that land in consequence has little, if any, selling value.

Regarding imports there is one important point to be borne in mind, namely that, at any given level of productivity and real income per person, a larger country is more likely to find opportunities of production within its own borders, and therefore to require less imports per head, than a smaller. To state the issue more precisely, if country B has only half the real income per head of country A, but twice the population, so that the aggregate real incomes of the two countries are the same, then their imports may also be expected to be about the same in volume. Attempts to explain volume of imports per head for various countries at different times as a function of real income per head have not proved very satisfactory. But an analysis[1] by one of the authors of imports as a function of total national product, irrespective of whether its size was due to population or to high per head income, proved satisfactory. (After all, it is the scale of the market which determines the possibility of establishing a greater variety of industries in a country, largely irrespective of whether the market has arisen through size of population, or through level of real income per head.) A range of cases in which aggregate net real product, measured in dollars of 1950 purchasing power, ranged from less than 1 billion (Norway and Finland in 1913) to 350 billion (United States at the present time), showed in general imports varying about with the three/fourth power of national

---

[1] *Monthly Bulletin of the Banque Nationale de Belgique*, July 1953. Subsequent unpublished work has also been drawn upon.

CHART XVIII.

THE INCOME ELASTICITY OF DEMAND FOR IMPORTS

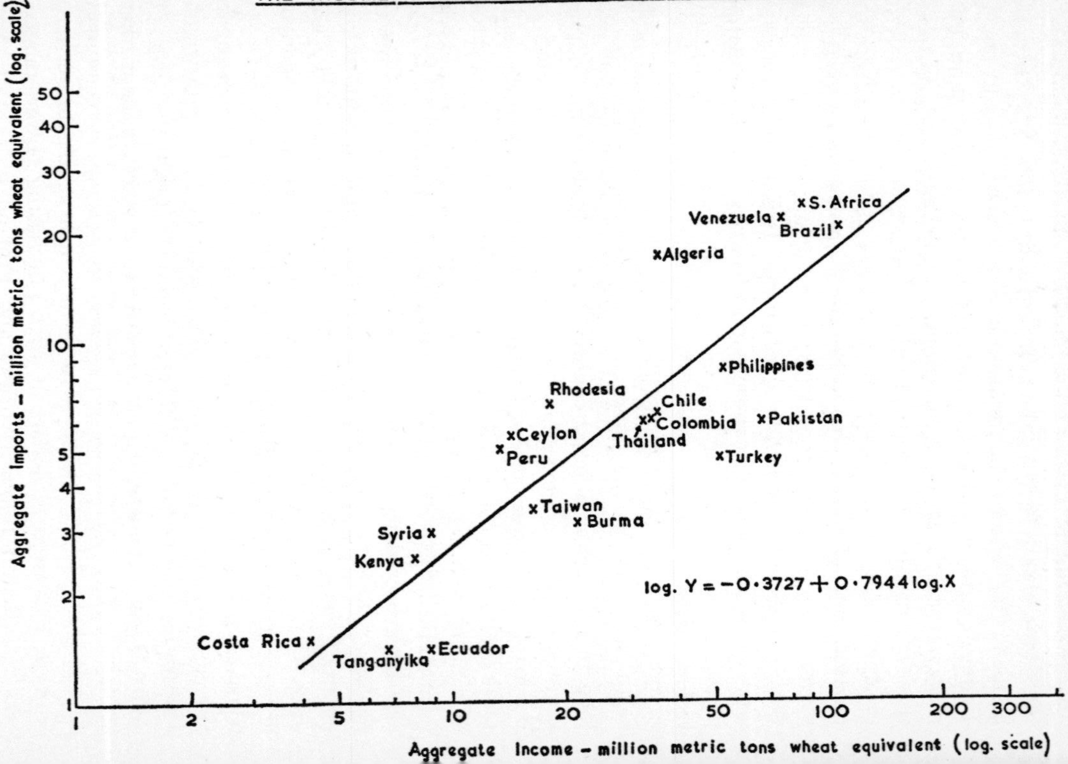

$$\log. Y = -0.3727 + 0.7944 \log. X$$

Aggregate Income – million metric tons wheat equivalent (log. scale)

Aggregate Imports – million metric tons wheat equivalent (log. scale)

product, subject to certain qualifications for particular countries, explainable in terms of their geographical situation, or tariff policy.

This conclusion was confirmed in quite an interesting way for Japan by a time-series analysis of the 1924–37 data.[1] It was found that changes in the logarithm of the volume of imports were well explained by 0·74 times the logarithm of real national income plus 0·279 times the logarithm of the terms of trade. The coefficient of 0·74 agrees well with that estimated from inter-country comparisons.

For the subsistence agriculture countries, however, the income elasticity of demand for imports appears to be higher than the figure of approximately three-quarters deduced for the richer countries. The comparatively low imports of India in relation to production, shown on the diagram, are to be explained, not in terms of high income per head, but of large population and high *total* product. We should, however, also bear in mind, in India's case, the very severe official restrictions placed upon imports, and the over-valuation of the rupee. It must be repeated once again that this analysis is not based on incomes per head, but on aggregate income.

The countries included in this diagram were those for which the United Nations give national product statistics. It is in respect of agricultural production, in subsistence agriculture countries, that there are the greatest discrepancies in methods of valuation. For agricultural production therefore we have used our own values, converted directly into wheat equivalents. For non-agricultural production we have taken the United Nations figures, in local currency, and converted to dollars at the current exchange rate (using the free market exchange rate where a system of multiple exchange rates prevailed). This method is crude and subject to very large errors.

The amount of agricultural produce which the subsistence agriculture countries will seek to sell on the world market will certainly increase during the coming decade. As is shown below, with the lowest assumption about productivity, and the highest assumption about their internal elasticity of consumption, the quantity offered for sale (including certain quantities of minerals, forest products, etc.) will rise from ten billion to thirteen billion dollars of present-day purchasing power. On the opposite assump-

[1] Tatemoto, Institute of Social and Economic Research, Osaka University, Discussion Paper No. 9.

tions however, of rapid productivity increase and low internal elasticity, the rise will be to over twenty-three billion dollars.

Another empirical discovery, which greatly simplifies analysis, is that in the early stages of development from subsistence agriculture it is permissible to treat average real income per head for the whole country as not very different from the agricultural productivity figure. It is true that average incomes per head in the non-agricultural pursuits are generally somewhat higher, but an important study by Umemura[1] for Japan, concerning the period of rapid economic growth from 1900 to 1920, shows comparatively slight differences, over this period, between average earnings of wage-earners in agriculture and in manufacture. The ratio between the earnings of labour in agriculture, and average net income produced per person engaged in agriculture, did not change much over the period, even though there were considerable oscillations in the rate at which labour was flowing from agriculture to industry. The principal effect of these temporary oscillations in the net rate of flow of labour into industry was to change wage-earnings (relative to profits) in industry. This study gives us a valuable idea of the mechanism of the flow of labour out of agriculture in a country emerging from subsistence economy. It appears to be, to a considerable extent, a self-regulating flow; if it becomes too rapid, industrial wages fall strongly, and discourage it for the time being.

From the relationship between the logarithm of agricultural productivity, and the number of non-agricultural workers as a proportion of the population, we can do some interesting algebra relating the rate of improvement of agricultural productivity, the rate of growth of population as a whole, and the absolute increase or decrease of agricultural population. During the period of the most rapid increase of Japanese agricultural productivity, between 1900 and 1925, agricultural production per head of rural population was rising at about 3·5 per cent per year; and agricultural population was about stationary. Rural population having been about 60 per cent of the whole at the beginning of the period, it can be shown that this stationariness of the absolute number of rural population would not have been compatible with a rate of general population growth much higher than 1 per cent per annum. In other words, the rates of population growth in the neighbourhood of 2 per cent per annum or more now prevailing in many parts of the world are *not* compatible with stationary or declining absolute numbers of

[1] Umemura, *Economic Survey of Japanese Agriculture*, 1956.

TABLE XXXVII. EXPECTED INCREASES IN AGRICULTURAL PRODUCTION AND EXPORTS OF THE SUBSISTENCE AGRICULTURE COUNTRIES ON VARYING ASSUMPTIONS OF INCOME ELASTICITY OF DEMAND FOR FOOD AND RATE OF PRODUCTIVITY INCREASE

| | Main-land China | India | Countries of Productivity: kg. economic wheat equivalent/head of population | | | | | | | | | TOTAL | Total $ bill. of 1960 purchasing power |
			below 550	550–675	675–826	826–1012	1012–1240	1240–1520	1520–1861	over 1861		
Population growth 1953–60, % p.a.	1·7	1·9	1·9	2·0	2·1	1·3	3·0	3·1	2·5	3·0		
1960 population (m.)	677	433	103	166	219	67	90	125	31	7	1918	
1960 agricultural population	547	366	84	124	163	48	60	81	19	4·4	1496	
1970 expected population (on above growth rate)	800	521	124	202	269	76	121	169	40	9·4	2331	
In m. tons wheat equivalent:												
1960 production	184	174	42	79	128	44	68	112	30·6	9·0	870	
1960 net export	–6	21	1	15	28	11	18	34	12·9	5·3	137	10·1
On 1% p.a. productivity increase:												
1970 agricultural population (m.)	633	397	99	147	196	53	79	107	23·7	5·8	1740	
1970 production	235	228	55	104	170	54	98	163	42·4	13·1	1162	
1970 net export (elasticity 0·7)	–5	31	2	20	38	14	27	50	18	8	203	13·1
1970 net export (elasticity 0·3)	4	38	3	23	40	16	30	54	19	8	227	14·6
On 3% p.a. productivity increase:												
1970 agricultural population (m.)	605	378	95	140	187	50	74	101	22·3	5·5	1657	
1970 production	273	264	64	120	197	62	113	187	48·5	15·0	1343	
1970 net export (elasticity 0·7)	–2	38	3	24	46	16	31	57	21	9	243	15·6
1970 net export (elasticity 0·3)	28	63	10	35	63	22	40	72	24	10	367	23·6

agricultural population, except in countries where the agricultural population is already a small proportion of the whole. Where it is 30 per cent or more, as it is in all the subsistence agriculture countries, further increases in the absolute numbers (though decreases in the relative numbers) of people engaged in agriculture must be expected for a long period to come, however high the rates at which agricultural productivity is increasing.

We may make some tentative predictions for a decade of growth on two widely varying assumptions, namely of the productivity of the agricultural population growing by 1 per cent and by 3 per cent per year. (Each country's output of non-agricultural 'exportable

Countries Included with Population in Millions

Productivity below 550		Productivity 550-675		Productivity 675-826	
Libya	1	Former French West Africa	20	Former French Equatorial Africa	4
Guinea	3	Tanganyika	9	Nigeria	35
Somaliland	2	Togo	1	Egypt	26
Haiti	4	Kenya	7	Congo and Ruanda Urundi	20
Afghanistan	14	Ethiopia	20	Madagascar	5
Former Indochina	37	Uganda	7	Sierra Leone	2
Korea	33	Jordan	2	Guatemala	4
Nepal	9	Lebanon	2	Honduras	2
		Pakistan	93	Indonesia	93
		Yemen	5	Thailand	26
				New Guinea	2

Productivity 826-1012		Productivity 1012-1240		Productivity 1240-1520	
Angola	5	Liberia	1	Ghana	7
Sudan	12	Morocco	12	Brazil	71
Cameroons	4	Mauritius	1	Iran	20
Tunisia	4	El Salvador	3	Philippines	28
Algeria	11	Nicaragua	1		
Basutoland	1	Panama	1		
Mozambique	6	Ecuador	4		
Bolivia	3	Peru	11		
Burma	21	British Guiana	1		
		Ceylon	10		
		Taiwan	11		
		Cyprus	1		
		Syria	5		
		Turkey	28		

Productivity 1520-1861		Productivity over 1861	
Rhodesia-Nyasaland	8	Malaya	7
Costa Rica	1		
Dominican Republic	3		
West Indies	3		
Colombia	14		
Paraguay	2		

products' is, for convenience, included here.) The calculation includes all the low-income countries of the world, not only the subsistence economies, but also those others whose exports for the next decade may be expected to be predominantly agricultural. Countries which have already reached a considerable degree of industrialization, such as Mexico, Japan, Chile, South Africa and Australia, are, however, excluded. For convenience in calculation, India and mainland China are shown separately, and the other countries grouped in ranges of exportable production/head of agricultural population, measured in kg. grain equivalent/person.

Within each of the two differing assumptions about the rate of growth of productivity, two further alternative assumptions are made, of a maximum of 0·7, and a minimum of 0·3, for income elasticity of demand for food.

In every case, it will be seen, a large increase in the agricultural population is expected during the decade. The higher assumption about the productivity growth, as we have postulated, requires a lesser rate of growth in agricultural population, but a greater rate of growth in total product.

The poorer countries require to eat all they produce, or more in some cases. China, for example, is unlikely to produce any substantial exportable surplus in the next ten years, unless both a high rate of productivity growth is obtained, and income elasticity of demand for food is kept down.

Of the exportable surplus produced by all the countries under review, nearly half comes from those whose productivity already stands at over 1000 units.

The world total of exports of food, raw materials and fuel in 1960, including exports from the Communist countries,[1] was $62 billion. Of this total, 22½ per cent represented fuels, mostly petroleum. (Contrary to general impression, the ratio of the value of trade in petroleum to the trade in other raw materials and food has declined slightly since 1955.)

The countries covered by the above table do not include many oil-producing countries. The net exports of these countries covered only amounted to 18 per cent of the world total of exports of food, raw materials, and fuels. One tends to forget that nearly half the world's exports of these commodities come from what the United Nations calls 'economically developed countries', i.e. North America, western Europe, Japan and Australasia; and a consider-

[1] United Nations, *Monthly Bulletin of Statistics*, March 1962.

able further amount from other countries too wealthy to be included in the above table, not all of them oil-producing countries.

Between 1950 and 1960[1] the volume of world exports of food, raw materials and fuels (excluding the Communist countries) rose by 64 per cent, or at an average rate of 4·1 per cent per year. Between 1957 and 1960 (two years chosen as occupying roughly analogous positions in the trade cycle) the rate of growth (including the Communist countries) was 5·8 per cent per year. This rate of growth of volume of supplies of food, raw materials and fuels has had injurious effects on the world terms of trade for primary producers, which fell by more than 15 per cent between 1957 and 1960.

These worsening terms of trade for primary producers, including many of the world's poorest communities, constitute a very serious problem, which will not readily be put right. The natural reaction of producers and their representatives is to demand from the richer and more powerful nations who are their customers that they should take the steps to 'stabilize' the prices of the principal products concerned; failing to realize that such stabilization is quite impossible, except for very short periods, without restriction of production, or perhaps even the organized destruction of surpluses.

The wealthier countries should, however, stop making the problem worse by subsidizing their own farmers.

The additional production evoked by subsidization and guaranteed prices in North America and western Europe is difficult to estimate; but it has undoubtedly played a considerable part in helping to turn the terms of trade against agriculture in the world market.

But why not allow farmers in North America and western Europe to go on producing as much as they can, at any price within reason, and give away the surplus food to the poorer parts of the world? This is a question asked by many people, not only by farmers. Many of those who reason this way have been influenced by the belief, now shown to be entirely erroneous, that two-thirds of the world was starving. Others may be agricultural politicians, who believe that they have found an easy way out of an intractable problem. Some are proposing that this giving away of surpluses should be 'internationally organized'. This sort of talk is having the particularly harmful consequence of leading many innocent far-

[1] Data from United Nations *Statistical Yearbook*.

mers to believe that it is going to be all right for them to go on producing surpluses, and that the United States Treasury will then pay for their disposal.

While occasional gifts of food in a bad season may be very welcome, the governments of most of the potential receiving countries themselves are very hesitant about agreeing to any scheme for receiving permanently gifts of food, or sales at particularly low prices. The government of India, for instance, rightly points out the paramount necessity of improving India's own agricultural productivity. The continued receipt of large supplies from abroad would have a discouraging effect here.

All the available studies on the demands of subsistence agricultural communities which we have assembled above have shown that, while a certain amount of additional food would be very welcome, their most urgent needs, on which they would like to spend any cash or the equivalent of cash which becomes available to them, are now for better clothing, housing, medicine and so forth.

In any case, even if some international system for giving away food could be organized, its administrators would wish to buy food as cheaply as they could, not to accept high-cost surpluses. Countries which make their living by exporting agricultural produce at low cost would also have a legitimate grievance against anyone who displaced them from their markets with subsidized food surpluses from elsewhere. A consequence of such a programme would also be, amongst other things, still further to worsen the world terms of trade against agricultural products.

We have no information at present on which to make an estimate about the growth of exports of food and raw materials from the economically advanced countries which supply the larger proportion of the world market to-day; but we may well expect it to continue even more rapidly than in the past decade. (Several of these countries, particularly Australia and Canada, are already in considerable balance of payments difficulties, which can only be put right by increasing their exports.) Against this background, the need of the poorer countries to extend their exports of agricultural products by anything from 30 to 130 per cent over the next decade (according to our various assumptions about elasticity of demand and growth of productivity) may well pose very serious problems for them, with the further movement of the terms of trade against them.

If it is not desirable, or even practicable, for us to give any substantial assistance to the poorer countries of the world by giving away high-cost surpluses produced by our own farmers, how can we best give them that help, which we certainly have an obligation to give? If not in food, then in money, in some form or other. To governments? There are further difficulties here. Let us quote from Professor Sir Dennis Brogan, addressing the International Investment Conference in Cambridge in July 1962:

'A great deal of the aid given by the Atlantic Community over the last ten years — for example, all the American money spent in Afghanistan — has been wasted. The only valuable thing done there in the last fifteen years was the introduction of the long-handled spade, which was a very important achievement, but it could have been done more cheaply.

If you give to a country with a very inadequate governing class, a very low level of public spirit, and a very low level of technical competence, you must attach conditions. Not only will the money be stolen — that does not shock me as much as perhaps it should — but it will be wasted, because the leaders of these countries have no idea of what is needed. I have talked to many of them — some are ex-pupils of mine. Given public opinion in their own countries, they cannot be trusted with the money, because it will be wasted on trivial or extravagant or absurd projects.

The injection of more money, without control and without any clear idea of the effect on the economy, is worse than nothing. It makes enemies; it does not make friends. It damages the recipients.

We have got to point out that many technical advances are only made possible given a certain political and legal framework. The greatest invention of the eighteenth century was not the steam engine but the limited liability company. Both of them were invented in Scotland, it is hardly necessary to say.

While it may appear natural and profitable in some countries to enforce one-party rule, a great deal of the immense technical advance of the Atlantic Community comes from the old legal tradition of power independent of government. The Japanese also, though this is very seldom recognized, had built up a very elaborate system of independent business corporations before the white man ever landed there.'

In the development of subsistence economies, governments undoubtedly have an important part to play; most of all in the earliest stages of economic development. In spite of all his strictures, 'in a country that has no business class, it is necessary to support state enterprises', Sir Dennis continued.

The problem is how to give aid in such a way as to help independent producers and traders to flourish, as well as governments.

The best way open to us for doing this is to give encouragement to all the enterprises in those countries, governmental or individual, which can produce goods for export. For in all but the very largest countries, a rapid increase in imports will be necessary, to provide not only capital equipment, but also the textiles, building materials, medicines and other commodities, the need for which is so urgently shown by all our consumption studies. As things are now, exporting from these countries has been made more difficult not only by the adverse movement of the world terms of trade (for which our own subsidized agricultural production is to a considerable degree responsible), but also by the tariffs and import restrictions which we impose on many of the simply processed manufactures which they try to export. There seems to be the strongest possible case for encouraging such exports of manufactured goods rather than discouraging them; and also for encouraging further exports of all agricultural products, except those whose markets are facing unmanageable surpluses.

Instead of taxing or restricting their exports, therefore, we should subsidize them.

It is desirable that all the countries agreeing to participate in such a scheme, and to pay a subsidy on the exports from the subsistence agriculture countries, should pay at the same rate. Otherwise the pattern of trade may be considerably distorted. The scheme could be best organized if all the benefactors were to pay their funds, available for this purpose, into a pool, out of which the subsidies would be paid at a uniform rate — which rate might have to be adjusted from time to time, according to changes in the amount of trade, and of money available. The subsidies should be paid *ad valorem*.[1]

In return for these concessions, the poorer countries would in return give free access to each other's goods. The promotion of freedom of trade, and specialization of production between these rapidly developing countries, perhaps even customs unions eventually, is very desirable. At the same time, however, they would

[1] The existence of a group of countries, which had paid a subsidy on all the exports received from the subsistence agriculture world, might lead to prices within the subsidizing countries being lower than elsewhere in the case of commodities such as groundnuts or cocoa, supplies of which come mainly from the subsistence agriculture countries. This situation may call for an export tax, at the same rate as the subsidy, payable on these goods if re-exported. Otherwise, trade might be considerably distorted by other countries purchasing these products, or goods incorporating them, in an indirect manner through the subsidizing countries.

retain the right to put restrictions and tariffs on goods from wealthier countries. The case for the protection of what are genuinely infant industries was perfectly well stated by John Stuart Mill over a hundred years ago. It remains valid, so long as the protection does not continue for too long. It is, however, only the poorer countries who should now claim this right. The richer countries should abrogate altogether the right of imposing direct restrictions, which do most harm to international trade, and should accept some limitation on the rates of tariff which they impose.

It is suggested that all the richer countries should agree to open their markets to such goods, and all to pay the funds which they have available for aiding the poorer countries into a single pool. This fund would be used to pay counter-tariffs, or subsidies, on all exports from the specified countries, at *ad valorem* rates, which might have to be varied a little from time to time.

For the purposes of this proposal, the countries of the world would be divided into four classes:

Class I countries — Urgently needing expanded markets for primary or simple manufactured exports, and also needing financial assistance.

Class II countries — Needing expanded markets for primary or simple manufactured exports, though less urgently than Class I, and not needing direct financial aid.

Class III countries — Capable of making limited economic sacrifices in order to accept more exports from above countries.

Class IV countries — Capable of making larger economic sacrifices in order to accept such exports, and also capable of making a direct financial contribution.

Trading relations between these four classes of countries should be as follows:

TABLE XXXVIII. PROPOSALS FOR INCREASING IMPORT AND EXPORT TRADE IN DEVELOPING COUNTRIES

		GOODS EXPORTED FROM:			
		Class I countries	Class II countries	Class III countries	Class IV countries
GOODS IMPORTED INTO:	Class I countries	No restrictions or tariffs	No restrictions Tariffs not to exceed 50%	Restrictions and tariffs may be imposed	Restrictions and tariffs may be imposed
	Class II	No restrictions Tariffs not to exceed 10%	No restrictions Tariffs not to exceed 25%	No restrictions Tariffs not to exceed 50%	Restrictions and tariffs may be imposed
	Class III countries	No restrictions or tariffs	No restrictions Tariffs not to exceed 10%	No restrictions Tariffs not to exceed 25%	No restrictions Tariffs not to exceed 50%
	Class IV countries	No restrictions or tariffs Subsidized	No restrictions or tariffs	No restrictions Tariffs not to exceed 10%	No restrictions Tariffs not to exceed 25%

Appendix

Grains

Wheat	1·00
Wheat-flour	1·43
Rice, rough	0·80
Rice, clean	1·19
Rye	0·75
Barley	0·65
Oats	0·65
Maize	0·75
Millet	0·68
Sorghum	0·60
Buckwheat	0·65
Other grains (as maize)	0·75

Starchy roots

Potatoes	0·65
Sweet potatoes	0·30
Cassava	0·23

Vegetable oils and oilseeds

Coconuts, shelled	2·52
Groundnuts, shelled	1·83
Groundnuts, unshelled	1·10
Linseed	1·45
Cotton seed	0·87
Soybeans	1·30
Vegetable oils	3·00

Sugar

Sugar, raw	1·03
Sugar, refined	1·10
Sugar-cane	0·147

Pulses

All pulses	1·12

Fish	3·50

Fruit

Citrus	0·92
Other fresh fruit	0·68
Bananas	0·32
Cider fruit	0·10
Raisins	2·50
Dates	1·30

Vegetables

All vegetables	0·65

Wine	0·90

Livestock products

Beef and veal	6·00
Pork	7·61
Mutton and lamb	7·25
Poultry	9·86
Milk	1·30
Eggs	5·80

Fibres

Abaca	2·20
Cotton, ginned	6·50
Cotton, unginned	2·94
Flax	6·08
Hemp	5·43
Henequen	1·90
Jute	2·00
Sisal	2·20
Wool, greasy basis	11·9
Silk cocoons	12·5

Other crops

Cocoa	4·50
Coffee	5·60
Tea	9·00
Tobacco	8·00
Rubber	5·18

The weighting system is based on data given in *International Index*

Numbers of Food and Agricultural Production by M. I. Klayman, FAO Monthly Bulletin of Agricultural Economics and Statistics, Vol. IX, March 1960.

CONVERSION FACTORS

1 kilometre	= 0·621372 miles
1 mile	= 1·609 kilometres
1 hectare	= 2·4711 acres
1 acre	= 0·4047 hectares
100 hectares	= 1 square kilometre
640 acres	= 1 square mile
1 square kilometre	= 0·3861 square miles
1 square mile	= 2·590 square kilometres
1 kilogramme	= 2·2046 lb.
1 lb.	= 0·4536 kilogrammes
1 metric ton	= 1000 kilogrammes
1 long ton	= 2240 lb.
1 short ton	= 2000 lb.
1 long ton	= 1·016 metric tons
1 short ton	= 0·9072 metric tons
1 metric ton	= 0·9842 long tons
1 metric ton	= 1·1023 short tons
1 metric ton kilometre	= 0·6116 long ton miles
1 metric ton kilometre	= 0·6849 short ton miles
1 long ton mile	= 1·635 metric ton kilometres
1 short ton mile	= 1·460 metric ton kilometres

DEFINITIONS

Economic rent: takes account only of payments for the use of land. Normal 'contract rent' also includes payment for the use of buildings or other fixed equipment. Taxes, rates, tithes etc. payable on land to be *included* in computing economic rent.

Average product per man-hour: total product divided by the total number of hours of labour applied to the same land.

Marginal product per man-hour: the additional product obtained when an additional man-hour of labour is applied to the same land.

Disguised unemployment: the state of affairs which exists when the same output could be produced using *less* labour. In this case the marginal product of labour is zero. A less extreme form of disguised unemployment is found when labour continues to work on family farms (or, sometimes, in certain other types of business) at a marginal productivity which, while not zero, is well below wages currently payable for such work.

Income elasticity of demand: the proportional change in the quantity of a good bought divided by the proportional change in income, price remaining the same.

Marginal propensity to consume: the proportion of an increment in income which will be consumed on a given commodity. For example, suppose income rises from £100 to £110 and expenditure on food changes from £70 to £75. Income elasticity of demand is $5/70 \div 10/100 = 0 \cdot 714$. The marginal propensity to consume food is $5/10 = 0 \cdot 5$. The two concepts must not be confused.

Price elasticity of demand: the proportional change in the quantity of a good bought divided by the proportional change in the price of the good, money income remaining the same. If the proportional change in quantity is less than the proportional change in price, demand is said to be inelastic; if the proportional change in quantity is greater than the proportional change in price, demand is said to be elastic. If price falls (rises) the total amount spent on a good will fall (rise) when demand is inelastic, and rise (fall) when demand is elastic. Price elasticity depends upon the possibilities of substitution. It is generally greater when substitution is easy. In low-income groups, however, there are few substitution possibilities.

Real income: the goods and services which a person can buy with his money income. With a *given* money income, real income will be higher when prices are low and vice versa.

Total product: the total money value of all goods (including services) which are produced, valued either at factor cost, that is by summing the costs of all factors of production which were required to produce them; or at the market prices consumers pay for them. Total product at market prices equals total product at factor cost less indirect taxes levied on the goods *plus* any subsidy payments.

Real product: total product corrected for price changes. A rise in the money value of total product as between two periods does not necessarily mean that real product has increased — it may simply represent the result of increased prices. Real product is essentially a *volume* concept.

Wheat equivalent: this is the natural unit for measuring real product in communities in which the greater part of the output is grain, grown for subsistence consumption with only a small and unrepresentative part of it traded for money. Since the output of other products is comparatively small and uncertainties about their valuation unlikely to affect the result appreciably, these are converted into grain equivalents at the rate at which they exchange against grain in local markets.

List of Authorities Cited

ANDREEV, V. N. and SAVKINA, Z. P., *International Grassland Conference*, 1960

BAER, G., *A History of Landownership in Modern Egypt*

BALDWIN, K. D. S., *The Niger Agricultural Project*, Blackwell, Oxford 1957

BECKETT, W. H., *Akosoaso*, London School of Economics Monograph in Social Anthropology, No. 10

BENNETT, M. K., British Wheat Yield Per Acre for Seven Centuries, *Economic History*, February 1935

BENNETT, M. K., *The World's Food*, New York 1954

BENNETT, M. K., *The Food Economy of the New England Indians, 1605–1675*. Repr. from The Journal of Political Economy, Vol. LXIII, No. 5, October 1955

BILLINGS, W. D., *Physiological Ecology*. Annual Review of Plant Physiology, Vol. VIII 1957

BITTERMAN, *Die Landwirtschaftiche Produktion in Deutschland*, 1800–1950

BONNÉ, A., *Archiv Für Sozialwissenschaft*, 1933

BONNÉ, A., *Economic Development of the Middle East*, 1943

BOURNE, J., *Railways in India*, 1848

BRASS, W., *The Estimation of Total Fertility Rates from Data for Primitive Communities*, World Population Conference, 1954

BUCK, J. L., *Land Utilization in China*, 1937

BUCK, J. L., *Land Utilization in China*, Statistical Supplement, 1937

Les Budgets Familiaux des Salaries Africains en Abidjan, Cote d'Ivoire, August-September 1956

CHILDE, G., *What Happened in History*, 1954

CIPOLLA, C. M., *The Economic History of World Population*, 1962

CLARK, GRAHAME, *Archaeology and Society*, 2nd Ed., 1947

CLAYTON, E. S., Economic and Technical Optima in Peasant Agriculture, *Journal of Agricultural Economics*, May 1961

COCHRAN AND MILLAR, *The Age of Enterprise*

COMBE, *Niveau de Vie et Progrès Technique*

CONKLIN, H. C., *Hanunóo Agriculture*, a Report on an Integral System of Shifting Cultivation in the Philippines, *FAO Forestry Development Paper* No. 12, 1957

CULWICK, G. M., *A Dietary Survey among the Zande of the South-Western Sudan*, 1950

CUMBERLAND, KENNETH B., *Moas and Men: New Zealand about A.D 1250*. Geographical Review, April 1962

DACCA UNIVERSITY, Report on the Marketing of Jute in East Pakistan

D'AVENEL, *La Richesse Privée Depuis Sept Siècles*

DEANE, P. AND COLE, W. A., The Long Term Growth of the United Kingdom, International Association for Research in Income and Wealth Conference, 1959

DE ARLANDIS, *Weltwirtschaftliches Archiv*, September 1936

DE COURCEY-IRELAND, M. G., HOSKING, H. R. AND LOEWENTHAL, L. J. A., *An Investigation into Health and Agriculture in Teso*, Uganda, Entebbe, 1937

DE FOVILLE, *La Transformation des Moyens de Transport*

DE VRIES, E., World Population Conference, Rome 1954

DE YOUNG, J. E., *Village Life in Modern Thailand*, 1955

DHEKNEY, *Hubli City*, Karnatak University Dharwar

DISKALKAR, P. D., *Resurvey of a Deccan Village*, Indian Society of Agricultural Economics, 1960

DITTMER, C. G., An Estimate of the Standard of Living in China, *Quarterly Journal of Economics*, Vol. XXXIII, November 1918, No. 1

DOBBY, E. H. G., *South East Asia*, 1950

DORE, R. P., *Land Reform in Japan*, O.U.P., 1959

DOVRING, F., *Land and Labour in Europe*, 1900–1950, The Hague, 1956

East African Royal Commission, 1953–55, Report, on measures necessary to achieve an improved standard of living, including the introduction of Capital to enable Peasant Farming to develop, Cmd. 9475

EDEN, F. MORTON, *The State of the Poor*, 1797

EDWARDS, D., *An Economic Study of Small Farming in Jamaica*, 1961

ENQUETE NUTRITION, *Niveau de Vie, Subdivision de Bongouanou, 1955–1956*. Territoire de la Cote D'Ivoire

Family Budgets of Nineteen Cultivators in the Punjab, 1953–54, Punjab Board of Economic Enquiry, Publication No. 39

FAO NUTRITIONAL STUDIES, *Calorie Requirements;* No. 5, 1950; No. 15, 1957

Farm Management, Land Use and Tenancy in the Philippines, Central Experiment Station Bulletin No. 1, 1957

FEI, HSIAO AND CHANG, CHIH-I, *Earthbound China. A Study of Rural Economy in Yunnan*. Routledge and Kegan Paul, 1949

FIRTH, R., *Malay Fishermen, Their Peasant Economy*, Institute of Pacific Relations, 1946

Foreign Agriculture, U.S. Department of Agriculture, June 1945, For Sao Paulo

FRASER, J. M., The Character of Cities, *Town and Country Planning*, November 1955

FREEMAN, J. D., *Iban Agriculture*. Colonial Office Research Study No. 18, 1955

FRIEDMAN, M., *The Theory of the Consumption Function*, Princeton, 1957

FRYER, G. E., A few words concerning the hill people inhabiting the forests of the Cochin State, *Journal of the Royal Asiatic Society*, Vol. 3, 1868

FRYER, G. E., On the Khyeng people of the Sandoway district, *Journal of the Asiatic Society of Bengal*, Vol. XVIV Part 1, 1875

FUGGLES-COUCHMAN, N. R., *Some Production-Cost Figures for Native Crops in the Eastern Province of Tanganyika Territory*, East African Journal of Agriculture, March 1939

GALLETTI, R. WITH BALDWIN, K. P. S. AND DINA, I. O., *Nigerian Cocoa-Farmers. An Economic Survey of Yoruba Cocoa-Farming Families*, Oxford Univ. Press, 1956

GAMBLE, S. D., *Ting Hsien, A North China Rural Community*, 1954

GEDDES, W. R., *The Land Dayaks of Sarawak*. Colonial Research Study No. 14, H.M.S.O., 1954

GHATGE, M. B. AND PATEL, K. S., *Economics of Mixed Farming in 'Charotar' (Bombay Province)*, Indian Journal of Economics, 1942–3

GHOSH, A. AND DAS, A., *Problems of Sub-Marginal Farming in West Bengal*, Indian Journal of Agricultural Economics, Vol. V, No. 1, March 1950

GLYN-JONES, M., *The Dusun of the Penampang Plains in North Borneo*, Report to the Colonial Office (Unpublished)

GOKHALE INSTITUTE, *Poona, A Resurvey*, 1953

GOUROU, P., *Annuaire de College de France*, 1959–60, 1961

GOUROU, P., *The Standard of Living in the Delta of the Tonkin*. Institute of Pacific Relations, 9th Conference, French Paper No. 4, 1945

GOUROU, P., *The Tropical World*, 3rd Edition, 1961

GRAY, M., *The Highland Economy, 1750–1850*, Edinburgh, 1957

GUILLARD, J., Essai de Mesure de L'activité du Paysan Africain: Le Toupourri, *Agronomie Tropicale*, Vol. XIII, No. 4, July-August 1958

HANCE, WILLIAM A., *African Economic Development*, O.U.P., 1958

HASWELL, M. R., *The Changing Pattern of Economic Activity in a Gambia Village*, Department of Technical Co-operation Overseas Research Publication No. 2, 1963

HASWELL, M. R., Economics and Population in Africa, *The Month*, November 1960

HASWELL, M. R., *Economics of Agriculture in a Savannah Village*, Colonial Research Studies No. 8, 1953

HAWKINS, E. K., *Road Transport in Nigeria*, O.U.P., 1958

HAWKINS, E. K., *Roads and Road Transport in an Underdeveloped Country. A Case Study of Uganda*. Colonial Office Research Study No. 32, 1962

HEADS, J., Urbanization and Economic Progress in Nigeria, *South African Journal of Economics*, Vol. 27, No. 3, September 1959

HERLIHY, DAVID, *Agricultural History*, April 1959

HIGBEE, EDWARD C., *The Agricultural Regions of Guatemala*, Geographical Review, April 1947

HIGGS, J. W. Y. WITH KERKHAM R. K. AND RAEBURN, J. R., *Report of a survey of problems in the mechanization of native agriculture in tropical African colonies*, Colonial Office, 1950

HOLMBERG, A. R., *Nomads of the Long Bow: The Siriono of Eastern Bolivia*, Smithsonian Institute of Social Anthropology, Publication No. 10, 1950

INDIA GOVERNMENT, *Studies in the Economics of Farm Management*, Bombay, 1954–55

INDIA GOVERNMENT, *Studies in the Economics of Farm Management*, Madras, 1954–55

INTERNATIONAL ASSOCIATION FOR INCOME AND WEALTH CONFERENCE, De Pietersberg 1957

INTERNATIONAL BANK FOR RECONSTRUCTION AND DEVELOPMENT, *Economic Development of Ceylon. Report of a Mission Organized . . . at the Request of the Government of Ceylon.* John Hopkins Press, 1953

INTERNATIONAL BANK FOR RECONSTRUCTION AND DEVELOPMENT, *Economic Development of Tanganyika. Report of a Mission Organized by the I.B.R.D. at the Requests of the Governments of Tanganyika and the United Kingdom.* John Hopkins Press, 1961

International Symposium on Desert Research, Jerusalem, 1952

IRAQ GOVERNMENT DEVELOPMENT BOARD, *Diyala and Middle Tigris Projects*, Report No. 3, 1959

ISOBE, H., *Farm Planning with special reference to the Management and Improving of small-scale family farming*, Japanese Ministry of Agriculture, October 1956

ISSAWI, C., *Egypt at Mid-Century, An Economic Survey*, O.U.P., 1954

Italian Statistical Abstract, (English Version), 1954

IZIKOWITZ, K. G., *Lamet: Hill Peasants in French Indo-China*, 1951

JACKMAN, *Development of Transport in Modern England*, 1916

JASNY, NAUM, *Wheat Studies* (Stanford), March 1944

JOHNSON, A. C., Volume on Egypt in the Series, *Economic Survey of the Roman Empire*

JOHNSTON, BRUCE F. AND MELLOR, JOHN W., *The Nature of Agriculture's Contributions to Economic Development*, Stanford University, Food Research Institute Studies, Vol. I, No. 3, 1960

JONES, G. T. AND BASU, D., International Pattern of Demand for Foodstuffs in 1954. *Farm Economist*, Oxford, 1957

JØRGENSEN, *National Museets Arbejdsmark*, 1953

KABERRY, P., *Report on Farmer-Grazier Relations*, London University, Mimeographed, April 1959

KABERRY, P., *Women of the Grassfields:* A Study of the Economic Position of Women in Bamenda, British Cameroons; Colonial Research Publication No. 14, 1952

KANEDA, HIROMITSU WITH JOHNSTON, BRUCE F., Urban Food Expenditure Patterns in Tropical Africa, *Food Research Institute Studies*, Vol. II, No. 3, November 1961

KIMURA, *Annals of the Hitotsubashi University*, April 1956

KING, GREGORY, *Political Observations*

KLAYMAN, M. I., *International Index Numbers of Food and Agricultural Production*, FAO Monthly Bulletin of Agricultural Economics and Statistics, Vol. IX, March 1960

KRZYWICKI, *Primitive Society and its Vital Statistics*

KRASŎVEC, STANE, *The Meaning of Technical Change in the Context of the Agricultural Economy of South-Eastern Europe*, International Conference of Agricultural Economists, 1955

KYOTO UNIVERSITY RESEARCH INSTITUTE OF FARM ACCOUNTING, No. 1, *The Report of Investigation of Family Farm Economy in 1956, Kinki District*, Japan 1959

LANDRY, A., *Traité de Démographie*, 1949

LEACH, E. R., Some Aspects of Dry Rice Cultivation in North Burma and British Borneo, *The Advancement of Science*, Vol. VI, No. 21, 1949

LEAGUE OF NATIONS, *Industrialization and Foreign Trade*, 1945

LEURQUIN, P. P., *Agricultural Change in Ruanda-Urundi*, 1945-60, Stanford, Food Research Institute, 1963

LOCKWOOD, W. W., *The Economic Development of Japan*, O.U.P., 1955

LYNN, C. W., *Agriculture in North Mamprusi*. Gold Coast Department of Agriculture Bulletin No. 34, 1937

McFIE, J., *Uganda Protectorate Nutrition Surveys, A comparison of the health of six villages consuming different types of food*, 1956

McGREGOR, I. A., Growth and Mortality in Children in an African Village, *British Medical Journal*, 23 December, 1961

MADRAS UNIVERSITY, Economic Series, No. 1, *Some South Indian Villages, A Resurvey*, Ed. P. J. Thomas, 1940

MANDAL, G. C., The Marketable Surplus of Aman Paddy in East Indian Villages, *Indian Journal of Agricultural Economics*, Vol. XVI, January-March 1961

MANOILESCO, *Welwirtschaftliches Archiv*, July 1935

MARTIN, ANNE, *The Oil Palm Economy of the Ibibio Farmer*, Ibadan University Press, 1956

MARUTA, S., *Memoirs of the Faculty of Agriculture*, Kagoshima University, No. 1, 1956

MASEFIELD, G. B., *Agricultural Change in Uganda*, Stanford University, Food Research Institute Studies, Vol. III, No. 2, 1962

MA YIN-CHU, *New Construction*, Peking, November 1959 (Chinese Text)

MELLOR, JOHN W. AND STEVENS, ROBERT D., *The Average and Marginal Product of Farm Labor in Underdeveloped Economies*, Journal of Farm Economics, 1956

MESZAROA, *Statisztika Szemle*, 1952

MICHELL, *The Economics of Ancient Greece*

MILLARD, R. S., Road Development in the Overseas Territories, *Journal of the Royal Society of Arts*, Vol. 107, March 1959

MITRANY, DAVID, *The Land and the Peasant in Rumania*

NADUJFALVY, *Revue Hongroise de Statistique*, 1947

NAYLOR, P. E., A Farm Survey of the New Hawija Settlement Project in Central Iraq, *Journal of Agricultural Economics*, Vol. XIV, No. 1, June 1960

NEWMAN, *Studies in the Import Structure of Ceylon*, Ceylon Planning Secretariat, October 1958

NOUGIER, L-R., *Population*, April-June 1954

Patterns of Income Expenditure and Consumption of African Unskilled Workers in Mbale, East African Statistical Department, Uganda Unit, 1958

PEDLER, F. J., *The Economic Geography of West Africa*, London 1955

PELZER, K. J., *Pioneer Settlement in the Asiatic Tropics*, New York 1954

PENROSE, E. F., *Food Supply and Raw Materials in Japan*, Chicago, 1930

PEPELASIS, A. A., WITH YOTOPOULOS, *Surplus Labour in Greek Agriculture, 1953–60*, Centre of Economic Research, Athens, Research Monograph No. 2

PETERS, D. U., *Land Usage in Serenje District*, Rhodes-Livingstone Paper No. 19, 1950

PETTY, SIR WILLIAM, *Political Arithmetick*

PHILLIPS, P. G., The Metabolic Cost of Common West African Agricultural Activities, *Journal of Tropical Medicine and Hygiene*, Vol. 57, No. 12, 1954

PING-TI HO, *Studies in the Population of China*, 1368–1953, Harvard University Press

PIRIE, N. W., *Future Sources of Food Supply: Scientific Problems*, Journal of the Royal Statistical Society, Series A, Vol. 125, Part 3, 1962

PLATT, B. S., *Nyasaland Nutrition Survey*, 1938–39, Colonial Office Library, Mimeographed

PLATT, B. S., *Tables of Representative Values of Food commonly used in Tropical Countries*, Medical Research Council Special Report No. 302, 1962

POSTAN, M. M., *Economic History of Europe*

PRIEBE, H., *Neuzeitliche Familienbetriebe*, Heft 1, Forschungsstelle Für Bäuerliche Familienwirtschaft E. V., Frankfurt Am Main, 1961

The Real Product of Soviet Russia, U.S. Senate Committee on the Judiciary, U.S. Government Printing Office, 1961

RESERVE BANK OF INDIA, *Rural Credit Follow-Up Survey, 1956–57*, Bombay 1960

RICARDO, DAVID, *Principles of Political Economy and Taxation*

RICHARDS, A. I., *Land Labour and Diet in Northern Rhodesia*, 1939

SARGENT, J. R., *Report on Transport Requirements in the Light of Economic Developments in North Borneo*, Colonial Office 1960

SARKAR, N. K., A Method of Estimating Surplus Labour in Peasant Agriculture in Overpopulated Underdeveloped Countries, *Journal of the Royal Statistical Society*, Series A, Vol. CXX, 1957

SAUER, CARL O., *Early Relations of Man to Plants*, Geographical Review, January 1947

SAUVY, A., *Population*, October-December 1953

SCHUSTER, W. H. WITH KESTEVEN, G. L. AND COLLINS G. E. P., *Fish Farming and Inland Fishery Management in Rural Economy*, F.A.O., 1954

SHASTRI, C. P., *Input-Output Relations in Indian Agriculture*, Indian Journal of Agricultural Economics, January-March 1958

SHASTRI, C. P., *Bullock Labour Utilization in Agriculture*. Economic Weekly, 29 October, 1960

SHAUM, *Economic History of Australia*

SHEN-PAO NIEN-CHIN, *Year Book*, Shanghai, 1933

SHIWALKAR, R. S., *Technique of Measuring Rural Unemployment*, Indian Journal of Agricultural Economics, March 1954

SHORTT, J., An account of some rude tribes, the supposed Aborigines of Southern India, *Transactions of the Ethnological Society*, Vol. III, 1865

SINGH, TALOK, *Poverty and Social Change*, 1945

SLATER, G. (EDITOR), *Some South Indian Villages*, University of Madras, Economic Series 1, 1918

SPENGLER, JOSEPH J., *Richard Cantillon: First of the Moderns*. I and II. Journal of Political Economy, August and October, 1954

SMITH, M. G., *The Economy of Hausa Communities in Zaria*, Colonial Research Study No. 16, H.M.S.O. 1955

SORBI, UGO, Borgo E Mozzano, Instituto Di Economica, University of Florence

SRINIVASAN, M. N., *Prices and Production Trends in Agriculture*, Indian Journal of Agricultural Economics, March 1954

Statistical Pocketbook of Indonesia, 1950

SUHA, A., *Economic Problems of Eastern Europe*

SWAMINATHAN, M. C., APTE, S. V. AND SOMESWARA RAO, K., *Nutrition of the People of Ankola Taluk (N Kanara)* Indian Journal of Medical Research, November 1960

TATEMOTO, Institute of Social and Economic Research, Osaka University, Discussion Paper No. 9

TAX, SOL, *Penny Capitalism, A Guatemalan Indian Economy*, Smithsonian Institution of Social Anthropology, Publication No. 16, Washington 1953

THOMAS, P. J. (EDITOR), *Some South Indian Villages, A Resurvey*, University of Madras, Economic Series 4, 1940

THOMSON, B. P., *Two Studies in African Nutrition: An Urban and a Rural Community in Northern Rhodesia*, Rhodes-Livingstone Paper No. 24, 1954

TOBATA, SEIICHI, *Japanese Agriculture*, 1952

TOTHILL, J. D., Agriculture in Uganda, O.U.P., 1940

TOTHILL, J. D., Agriculture in the Sudan, O.U.P., 1948

TOUTAIN, J. C., *Le Produit de L'Agriculture Française de 1700 a 1958*, Vol. II Cahiers de L'Institut de Science Economique Appliqué, Supplement No. 115, July 1961

TROWELL, H. C., Calorie and Protein Requirements of Adult Male Africans, *East African Medical Journal*, Vol. 32, No. 5, May 1955

TUTIYA, K., *Quarterly Journal of Agricultural Economics*, No. 1, 1955, in Japanese

UMEMURA, *Economic Survey of Japanese Agriculture*, 1956

United Nations Monthly Bulletin of Statistics, March 1962

United Nations Yearbook of International Trade Statistics, 1960

UNITED STATES DEPARTMENT OF AGRICULTURE, FAS-M 101, 104, 108, Parts II, III and IV, *Food Balances in Other Countries*, 1960–61

ERS-FOREIGN-34, *The Philippines: Long Term Projection of Supply and of Demand for Selected Agricultural Products*

U.S. SENATE, *The Real Product of the Soviet Union*, 1961

VAN BEUKERING, J. A., *Het Ladagvraagstuk, Een Bedrijfs — Ein Sociaal Economisch Probleem*, Mededeelingen Van Het Department Van Economische Zaken In Nederlandsch — Indie, No. 9, 1947

VANDELLOS, *Metron*, 1925

VAN DER KOPPEL, *Die Landbouw In Den Indischen Archipel*

VANZETTI, Società Italiana Di Sociologia Rurale, *Land and Man in Latin America*, 1961

WAIBEL, LEO HEINRICH, *Vegetation and Land use in the Planalto Central of Brazil*, Geographical Review, October 1948

WALBANK, *Cambridge Economic History of Europe*

WARRINER, D., *Land and Poverty in the Middle East*. Royal Institute of International Affairs, 1948

WARRINER, D., *Land Reform and Development in the Middle East. A*

Study of Egypt, Syria and Iraq. 1st Edition, 1948, 2nd Edition, 1962, Oxford Univ. Press

WELK, A. D., *Recent Economic Changes*, 1889

Wheat Production in Kenya, 1955–56, An Economic Study, Government Printer, Nairobi, 1957

WICKIZER, V. D. AND BENNETT, M. K., *The Rice Economy of Monsoon Asia*, California, 1941

WIJEWARDENE, R., *From Bullock to Tractor*, World Crops, Vol. 13, No. 11, November 1961

WILSON, P. N., An Agricultural Survey of Moruita Erony, Teso, *Uganda Journal*, Vol. 22, No. 1, March 1958

WILSON, P. N. AND WATSON, J. M., Two Surveys of Kasilang Erony, Teso, *Uganda Journal*, Vol. 20, No. 2, September 1956

WILSON, T. B., *Economics of Paddy Production in Northern Malaya*, Malayan Department of Agriculture, 1958

WINFIELD, G. F., *China, the Land and the People*, 1948

WINTER, E. H., *Bwamba Economy*, East African Institute of Social Research, 1956

World Population Conference, 1954

The World Today, Institute of International Affairs, March 1947

ZIMMERMAN, C. C., *Siam Rural Economic Survey, 1930–31*

Index

PRINTED IN GREAT BRITAIN BY ROBERT MACLEHOSE AND CO. LTD
THE UNIVERSITY PRESS, GLASGOW